MW00695379

THE NEW HUMAN REVOLUTION

VOLUME 12

THE NEW HUMAN REVOLUTION

VOLUME 12

DAISAKU IKEDA

ILLUSTRATIONS BY
KENICHIRO UCHIDA

World Tribune
—*Press*—

Published by World Tribune Press
606 Wilshire Boulevard
Santa Monica, California 90401

Complete Set   ISBN-13: 978-0-915678-32-7
               ISBN-10: 0-915678-32-2
Volume 12   ISBN-13: 978-0-915678-44-0
               ISBN-10: 0-915678-44-6

Interior and cover designed by Gopa & Ted2, Inc.

10 9 8 7 6 5 4 3 2 1

Contents

Editor's Note

The citations most commonly used in this book have been abbreviated as follows:

♦ GZ refers to the *Gosho Zenshu*, the Japanese-language compilation of letters, treatises, essays and oral teachings of Nichiren Daishonin.

♦ LS refers to *The Lotus Sutra*, translated by Burton Watson (New York: Columbia University Press, 1993).

♦ WND refers to *The Writings of Nichiren Daishonin* (Tokyo: Soka Gakkai, 1999).

Fresh Hope

MORNING NEVER FAILS to arrive. Morning represents hope. Those who have hope in their hearts readily welcome the dawn of a new day.

Let us begin afresh. Let us open wide the golden doors to a brilliant future. Let us open the doors of life. The cool breezes of a new century sweep through the air as gold and silver waves of hope dance on the vast blue sea.

Let the bells signaling a fresh departure in our lives ring loud and clear. Together with our friends and comrades in faith, we are setting out on a great voyage to fulfill our noble mission. It is a voyage that will decide our victory or defeat.

May 3, 1967. On this day, as on the same day seven years earlier when Shin'ichi Yamamoto became president of the Soka Gakkai, blue skies stretched overhead. The trees lining the streets of Tokyo were bathed in sunlight, their burgeoning leaves swaying gently in the breeze.

The Thirtieth Headquarters General Meeting, commemorating the seventh anniversary of Shin'ichi's inauguration, began amid high spirits at the Nihon University auditorium in Ryogoku, Tokyo.

Prior to the meeting, some twelve hundred members of the Soka Gakkai Brass Band and Fife and Drum Corps participated in a grand parade. A huge crowd of local residents, Soka Gakkai members included, stood along the parade route cheering and applauding the youths' dynamic performance. The sousaphone players marched the entire three-mile route carrying their thirty-three-pound tuba-like instruments on their shoulders. It no doubt required strenuous effort. The well-organized parade brimmed with youthful vigor and brilliance.

By just after eight o'clock in the morning, the Nihon University auditorium was filled to capacity. Across the front of the stage hung a white banner on which was written "Congratulations" in large red letters, followed by "Commemorating the Presidential Inauguration—Seventh Anniversary" in bold brush strokes.

The participants were in high spirits. As comrades in faith, they had fought alongside Shin'ichi in the movement to advance kosen-rufu, sharing both tears and laughter. Through this process, they had overcome various hardships and transformed their karma, savoring the true brilliance of life. It was therefore with a sense of boundless appreciation and joy that these friends had gathered together that day.

THE PARTICIPANTS tried to control their excitement as they waited for the meeting to begin.

The ancient Roman philosopher Seneca stated: "We are naturally disposed to admire more than anything else the man who shows fortitude in adversity."[1]

At half past eleven, congratulatory telegrams from overseas members were introduced. The members in Nigeria wrote: "President Yamamoto, please accept our heartfelt congratulations on the seventh anniversary of your inauguration. We are determined to dedicate ourselves to the realization of kosen-rufu in Africa."

Messages expressing the joy and resolve of members around the world were read one after another. Each was met with resounding applause.

The global advancement of kosen-rufu exemplified by these telegrams was the direct result of Shin'ichi Yamamoto's tireless endeavors. Thus far, he had made twelve overseas visits to five continents in an effort to encourage the spread of Nichiren Buddhism.

Shin'ichi entered the auditorium at the appointed time of noon amid the members' vigorous applause. The start of the meeting was then announced. Following opening words, General Administrator Kiyoshi Jujo reported on the progress made by the Soka Gakkai since Shin'ichi's inauguration as third president in 1960.

"In the last seven years, we have advanced tremendously and realized unprecedented achievements! Thanks to President Yamamoto's unflagging efforts, every wish of our mentor, second Soka Gakkai president Josei Toda, has come to fruition. At this time, I would like to introduce several of these accomplishments from various perspectives.

"Before President Yamamoto's inauguration, our organization comprised 1.4 million member-households, but in the past seven years, that number has grown to 6.25 million. The number of chapters has also increased from sixty-one to an incredible 3,393 in Japan alone.

"Furthermore, President Yamamoto has established the high school, junior high school and elementary divisions for our young phoenixes taking flight into the future. In this way, he has set in motion a mighty current that will produce capable successors of kosen-rufu. In order to promote culture, he has also formed the educators, artists and academic divisions. These groups have also developed many talented people in diverse fields.

"Meanwhile, in the area of music and art, he has founded the Min-On Concert Association with the aim of sending the light of humanistic culture into society. Additionally, the Institute of Oriental Philosophy (initially named the Institute of Oriental Studies) for academic research and the Clean Government Party have also been established.

"Currently, the construction of the Soka Junior High School and Soka High School are steadily progressing toward their opening next year, and preparations are under way as well for the opening of Soka University in the near future."

KIYOSHI JUJO next reported on developments in the Soka Gakkai outside of Japan. He announced that the overseas membership had grown to one hundred fifty thousand member-households and that a new temple was soon to open on the outskirts of Los Angeles in the United States.

In closing, he said: "I am firmly convinced that all our incredible advancement and growth is due to the selfless dedication of President Yamamoto. I would therefore like to convey our most heartfelt appreciation to him.

"Burning with the single-minded desire to repay our debt of gratitude to our mentor and filled with courage and fresh resolve, let us pledge together to realize even greater advancement in the next seven years!"

The members applauded vigorously, expressing their agreement with Jujo's sentiments.

Seeing the members' enthusiasm, Shin'ichi Yamamoto felt humbled. It was true that for the past seven years he had given every ounce of his being for kosen-rufu. He had worked so hard each day that he had barely spent any time at home. During that period, because of his weak constitution, he had fallen ill on numerous occasions. Nevertheless, when he thought of how his fellow members were counting on him, he couldn't slow down.

At the time of his inauguration as president, Shin'ichi had vowed to devote his life to the kosen-rufu movement and to supporting his fellow members. It was therefore only natural that he had exerted himself so intensely toward that end. He had hoped that to the extent he did so, the members would be able to concentrate on their Buddhist practice while getting plenty of rest and fully savoring the joys of life.

But the members threw themselves wholeheartedly into their Soka Gakkai activities with a spirit of total dedication to kosen-rufu. Shin'ichi had observed their sincere efforts each day, and it nearly moved him to tears. He felt that due to each member's courageous endeavors, the Soka Gakkai had developed so much in the last seven years.

After greetings by several other leaders, the auditorium erupted again in thunderous applause. It was finally Shin'ichi's turn to take the podium. His voice resonated with firm resolve as he spoke: "If we liken the activities of the Soka Gakkai to a sea voyage, we have been coasting close to the shoreline for the last seven years. But now that our training is completed, it is time for us to boldly set sail out into the vast Pacific Ocean, braving the rough seas as we aim single-mindedly toward our distant goal."

THE MEMBERS APPLAUDED joyously, their exuberance growing by the moment. They were all captivated by Shin'ichi's clear, resonant voice.

Shin'ichi continued: "The next seven years represent the second phase of our efforts to realize kosen-rufu. It will be an even more significant period than the one beginning with the founding of the Soka Gakkai and leading until now. It will be a time of solidifying the foundation of our movement, in which our ultimate victory or defeat will be determined.

"Our goal is to actualize the vision of Nichiren Daishonin and bring about lasting peace and prosperity for all humanity. I therefore hope you will become champions of faith who never retreat a single step, and that you will continue to struggle valiantly together with me as we advance into the future."

The participants applauded enthusiastically in response.

Shin'ichi then announced that the long-awaited construction of the Grand Main Temple at the head temple would be completed in 1972. This event, he said, would correspond with the end of the sixth of the Seven Bells, and mark the start of the seventh.[2] He noted that while numerous structures of prestige had been built around the world, they had often been created in the name of authority and at the cost of great suffering to many. The Grand Main Temple, on the other hand, was being constructed through the sincere and joyous contributions of ordinary people, Shin'ichi added, and it would be lauded globally as the sanctuary of the essential teaching of the people.

In a penetrating analysis of current social conditions, Shin'ichi next addressed the issue of human alienation. The way of life of a Buddhist practitioner is to squarely confront the real problems of society and to strive to resolve them.

Shin'ichi continued: "The various issues plaguing the minds of contemporary thinkers and intellectuals, such as the impasse civilization has reached, can ultimately be traced to the loss of our humanity, or human alienation. This stems from the fact that humanity's spiritual development has taken a backseat to the development of material and technological civilization, causing people to lose their sense of personal identity and resulting in a general disregard for the dignity of life.

"This phenomenon can be illustrated from several perspectives. For example, the mechanization of various aspects of daily life has rendered people subordinate to machines, whereby they are completely dependent on them. We are also witnessing an increase in layoffs by companies seeking to streamline and automate their businesses."

SHIN'ICHI YAMAMOTO continued his keen analysis of societal trends:

"As we can see with bureaucratic institutions, when organizations expand, people become reduced to mere cogs in the machinery. When this happens, the organization itself becomes a giant machine that functions beyond the wishes of the individual, causing him or her to be overcome by an indescribable sense of powerlessness and emptiness.

"It is also a sad reality that many people today, inundated with news and information from the mass media, simply accept what they are told without question. As this situation persists, people are losing the will to act on their own initiative, developing a weakened spiritual state in which they are always passively waiting for something to happen.

"Furthermore, the absence of a solid standard on

which people can base their lives and way of thinking is resulting in a general lack of sound judgment and, subsequently, actions predicated on pure impulse and instinct."

Shin'ichi went on to discuss the threat of nuclear weapons and other issues, demonstrating the reality of how people were being crushed by the advancement of technological and material civilization, becoming alienated from each other and society in the process.

Seeing this growing alienation, Shin'ichi felt a strong sense of crisis. For some time, he had been pondering how to resolve this situation for the sake of humanity's future. He therefore declared that surmounting this problem would require the establishment of a solid identity in people's lives so that they could freely utilize the power of technology for their own purposes. Toward that end, he added, it was critical that people adopt a philosophy or religion that could serve as a mainstay of their existence.

Pointing to the fact that both Christianity, on which the capitalism of the West was founded, and communism had reached a deadlock, Shin'ichi proclaimed that Nichiren Buddhism, the great philosophy of life that elucidates the principle of the oneness of body and mind,[3] had the power to open the way to a new spiritual civilization.

In closing, he stated with firm resolve: "Throughout our lifetime, no matter what storms may rage, let us continue to advance with the dignity of a mighty lion king and the lofty spirit of a soaring eagle. And, with the awareness that the Soka Gakkai is the king of the religious and philosophical world, let us, as disciples of Nichiren, carry out a proud struggle for the sake of the Law!"

SHIN'ICHI'S SPEECH brought a new perspective to the meeting participants. Many of them had developed strong conviction in Nichiren Buddhism through overcoming various financial, health and family hardships. But they were having a difficult time comprehending the role of Buddhism in solving such huge societal issues as human alienation.

Shin'ichi's declaration, however, that Buddhism offered the only solution to these problems served to deepen their faith even further. At the same time, it inspired in them a profound sense of mission and responsibility as Buddhists to take on the challenges facing humankind.

Last on the meeting schedule was the singing of Soka Gakkai songs. Eisuke Akizuki, who had been appointed the organization's general administrator in January of that year, led everyone in "Song of Victory." When he finished, the emcee called on Shin'ichi to lead a song. A wave of excited applause rippled throughout the auditorium.

Shin'ichi smiled as he nodded in agreement. He then stood up, fan in hand. The members cheered with delight.

Shin'ichi's conducting epitomized his role as the leader of the kosen-rufu movement. It was this kind of bold leadership that spurred the Soka Gakkai's victorious advance.

The valiant strains of "Song of Indomitable Dignity" began to play. The resonant sound of the members' unified clapping reverberated powerfully.

Into this defiled and evil world
We of the Gakkai go
Who would dare to block our way?

Shin'ichi led the song with majesty and grace. His movements were filled with his determination to lead the kosen-rufu movement over the next seven years.

Watching Shin'ichi, the members could feel his solemn resolve and they began to clap more vigorously in time with the music. Their eyes brightly sparkled.

The Headquarters general meeting thus came to a close with a joint pledge to initiate a fresh advance and achieve victory under President Yamamoto's leadership. The champions of Soka were setting forth anew into the hope-filled frontiers of kosen-rufu before them.

O N MAY 13, ten days after the Headquarters general meeting, Shin'ichi Yamamoto departed Japan on a guidance trip that would take him to the United States and Europe. He lost no time embarking on his worldwide activities to initiate the second phase of global kosen-rufu.

Shin'ichi could not rest even for a moment. He was resolved to live out his life in accordance with Nikko Shonin's admonition, "Until kosen-rufu is achieved, propagate the Law to the full extent of your ability without begrudging your life" (GZ, 1618). Indeed, this was what it meant to inherit Nichiren's teachings. It was the Soka Gakkai spirit.

Shin'ichi would first make stops in Hawaii, Los Angeles and New York in the United States. He would then travel to France, Italy, Switzerland and the Netherlands in

Europe. Accompanying him were his wife, Mineko, and several Soka Gakkai leaders, including General Director Hiroshi Izumida and General Administrator Kiyoshi Jujo. High Priest Nittatsu and other Nichiren Shoshu priests were also joining them in order to conduct Gohonzon-enshrinement ceremonies at temples in Honolulu and other locations.

Shin'ichi and his party departed Tokyo at half past ten in the morning on May 13, but because of the time difference, it was at around ten in the evening on the twelfth that they arrived in Honolulu.

At noon local time on the thirteenth, a Gohonzon-enshrinement ceremony was conducted at the newly established Honsei-ji temple. The sun shone brightly in the clear blue sky over this island of perpetual summer.

The temple was situated on a small hill about one mile away from the Soka Gakkai's Hawaii Community Center. Although the total Hawaii membership at the time was over two thousand member-households, the ceremony had to be limited to two hundred representative local members.

In October seven years earlier, when Shin'ichi visited Hawaii on the first of his journeys for worldwide kosen-rufu, only thirty or so people were present at the discussion meeting he attended. But the organization in Hawaii had developed such that it was currently the major base of activities in the entire Pacific region, having established first a community center and now a temple.

For those leaders accompanying Shin'ichi who were familiar with the situation back in 1960, it seemed like a completely different age. But while they were indeed astonished, no doubt none of them had considered what had actually been the driving force behind this amazing growth. In fact, it had been Shin'ichi's thoroughgoing encouragement of each member.

OUR ORGANIZATION, our movement, is sustained by individuals. When those people fundamentally transform their inner attitude, awaken to their life's mission and bring forth their highest potential, they can change anything. That is why the quiet, steady endeavor to guide and encourage people in faith is the very lifeblood of the kosen-rufu movement.

During his first trip to Hawaii, Shin'ichi Yamamoto devoted every moment he could to talking with the members. He also held question-and-answer sessions at discussion meetings where he would listen to the tearful accounts of members who desperately wanted to return to Japan. Empathizing with their sorrows, he warmly encouraged them. He made time for personal guidance sessions back at his hotel as well.

Shin'ichi poured himself patiently and unstintingly into such efforts, striving to plant seeds of mission and instill fresh hope in the members' hearts, thereby helping them transform their inner frame of mind. Whenever he visited Hawaii after that first trip, he continued to personally encourage as many members as possible.

The transformation of a person's inner resolve through dialogue is the key to achieving victory in all endeavors.

Shin'ichi was starting off the second phase of the movement to spread the Mystic Law—a period that would focus on the next seven years—from Hawaii, the place where he had taken his first steps in that noble endeavor seven years earlier. This thought filled him with deep emotion as he attended the enshrinement ceremony at Honsei-ji temple.

As in 1960, Shin'ichi was determined on this trip to meet with as many people as he could, encourage them and infuse their lives with a strong sense of mission. He knew that this was the best way to advance kosen-rufu.

He had a full itinerary, which included a number of scheduled activities and events as well as accompanying High Priest Nittatsu on his various engagements. Nevertheless, he made it his personal responsibility to encourage members each day.

After the enshrinement, a commemorative photo session was held, followed by a ceremony in which palm trees were planted on the temple grounds. In between, Shin'ichi spoke with one member after another, shaking their hands as he did so.

When the events at the temple were finished, Shin'-ichi headed immediately to the Hawaii Community Center, where members were waiting to see him. No sooner had he entered the building than he was surrounded by members wanting to shake his hand. He clasped their hands firmly, conveying his appreciation to each of them: "Thank you very much for all your efforts! I am so happy to see you!"

AS SHIN'ICHI YAMAMOTO shook hands with the members, he unceasingly encouraged them. To one elderly person, he said: "Please live long. Victory in life is not determined by fame or social position.

It is decided by how joyfully and dynamically you live out your life. Your living this way will be wonderful proof of the power of faith."

Shin'ichi then remarked to a young man standing nearby: "Please become a champion of faith. This means creating your own history of kosen-rufu without being defeated by your weaknesses. This is how I have lived my life, and I can confidently say that doing so becomes our greatest treasure."

Accurately discerning what was on each member's mind, Shin'ichi's words struck a deep chord in their hearts and caused a surge of joy and courage to well forth from within them.

That night, during a discussion back at the hotel, an American leader of Japanese descent asked Shin'ichi: "As I listened to you speak with the members, I was astonished at how you knew just what to say to each person. How do you do that?"

"It's because I am absolutely earnest," Shin'ichi replied.

He employed no secret or special technique.

Everything comes down to earnestness. When we are earnest, we tap into our courage, strength and wisdom. Earnest people are not rash, careless or negligent, and therefore they are not defeated. Their lives shine with sincerity and integrity.

Shin'ichi found just the right words because he poured his energies into every encounter with the attitude that he might never again have the opportunity to meet that person. Single-mindedly determined to grasp what each person was feeling, their struggles and their situations, he spoke to them from his heart, praying sincerely for their development and growth.

SHIN'ICHI CONTINUED to take every possible opportunity to inspire and invigorate members during his visit to the United States. For example, while moving from one activity to the next, he strove to encourage his driver, and when the young man asked him to name his baby, Shin'ichi obliged immediately. He was determined to do anything for the sake of his fellow members.

Even after a full day of activities, Shin'ichi would often stay up late into the night, writing words of encouragement on cards or in books to present to members. He wanted to forge a connection with each person.

The Soka Gakkai is not strong merely because an organizational structure exists. It is strong because it is built on heart-to-heart bonds between people.

On May 15, Shin'ichi and his party traveled to Los Angeles, and on the following day, they participated in a Gohonzon-enshrinement ceremony at the newly constructed Myoho-ji temple in Etiwanda, on the outskirts of the city. In the distance, the remaining snow atop the San Gabriel Mountains glistened in the sunlight. The sky was clear and a refreshing breeze rustled through the budding trees.

At eleven o'clock in the morning, when Shin'ichi arrived at the temple together with High Priest Nittatsu, the Brass Band struck up a valiant march. Their joyous performance celebrated the special occasion.

Myoho-ji temple was a modern, one-story wooden structure with high ceilings. A lawn had been planted on the grounds, along with a Japanese-style landscaped garden complete with a small hill, a pond and pine trees.

In order to prepare the land for construction, the grapevines and orange groves that had once covered it had been cleared, weeds had been painstakingly pulled, stones and rocks had been transported, and trees had been planted. The local members had taken on this hard labor entirely by themselves. They had volunteered their time enthusiastically with the thought that once a local temple had been built, they would no longer have to wait for a priest to come from Japan to issue Gohonzon, but could hold conferral ceremonies whenever necessary. They believed this would facilitate their efforts to advance kosen-rufu.

Shin'ichi was moved that these members had toiled covered in sweat and dirt under the blazing sun day after day to complete this arduous task. His gratitude toward them knew no bounds.

THE NIGHT BEFORE the enshrinement ceremony was to take place, Shin'ichi made a proposal to representative American leaders: "I have given much thought to how we can create a powerful current of kosen-rufu here in America, and how to support members in advancing with hope and joy. I would thus like to suggest making the organization here into a joint headquarters, as we have done in Europe and Southeast Asia, in order to lay a solid foundation for tremendous growth. What do you think?"

The leaders expressed their full agreement.

The next day, Shin'ichi introduced this new change at

the enshrinement ceremony. Addressing the gathering, he smiled and said: "America Headquarters has embarked on a new era and the second stage of its development. I would like to declare that kosen-rufu in America has now entered the essential phase.

"When the first Soka Gakkai chapter was established on my initial visit to the United States seven years ago, there were barely three hundred member-households. But now, your organization has grown into a headquarters consisting of thirty-nine chapters in nine joint chapters, with some thirty thousand member-households.

"Today, I would like to announce that after careful consideration, we have decided to make a fresh start into the future. The US organization will henceforth be a joint headquarters comprised of three headquarters—West Coast, East Coast and Hawaii."

The members cheered and applauded vigorously. They sensed that the time had come for American kosen-rufu to advance in earnest. They felt deep pride in the fact that the United States, as the country where President Yamamoto had taken his first steps outside of Japan in his journey toward world peace, was indeed the pioneer of the Soka Gakkai's global movement.

The announcement of the formation of a joint headquarters ignited a passionate fighting spirit in the hearts of the members, transforming their pride into a firm resolve that this second stage in the endeavor to realize worldwide kosen-rufu would also be launched from the United States. This was the perfect step in securing the groundwork for America's future progress.

Shin'ichi concluded his speech by sharing his profound wish that the American members would transcend all ethnic and cultural differences as they worked closely together to establish a democratic society founded on Buddhist ideals.

This was followed by the conferral of chapter flags and then a reception. Even during the party, Shin'ichi spared no effort in encouraging the members.

ON THE LAWN of the temple grounds, the women's division chorus, the Brass Band and the Fife and Drum Corps joyfully performed musical numbers. In addition to such Japanese favorites as "Moonlit Desert" and "Moon Over the Ruined Castle," they played some American pieces. After each song, Shin'ichi Yamamoto applauded heartily and expressed his praise for the performers.

When Shin'ichi learned that a band comprised of

select members of the Brass Band had been formed but didn't have a name yet, he offered the name the "Tribune Band." A tribune is someone who defends the rights of the people. Shin'ichi had chosen this name with the hope that these young men would dedicate themselves to protecting the people. He also wanted them to continue playing music that inspired people to have courage and to stand up for justice.

After the performances, Shin'ichi sat for commemorative photos with the various participants. A number of photos were taken. Everyone was delighted, but Shin'-ichi, who had been speaking with the members nonstop, was drenched in perspiration and his throat was parched.

Shin'ichi's wife, Mineko, kept smiling but was also watching her husband with an anxious eye. She knew better than anyone how taxing it was for Shin'ichi to stand in the sweltering heat and continue encouraging the members until his voice was hoarse.

Shin'ichi was sickly as a child and suffered from tuberculosis. While he was now in relatively good health, he still lacked physical stamina. Whenever he overexerted himself, he would invariably fall ill, often breaking out in a fever. But having pledged to dedicate his life to working for kosen-rufu, he would consistently push himself to the limit, and no one could persuade him otherwise.

Mineko, in the hopes of at least preventing Shin'ichi from catching a cold, was always prepared with towels and a change of clothes in case he became drenched in perspiration. And when they traveled overseas, she was even more mindful than usual of his meals. All the while, she would be chanting in her heart for her husband's health. It was impossible to fathom just how much Shin'-ichi had been protected by Mineko's careful consideration and attention over the years.

Shin'ichi poured his entire life into encouraging members. His words therefore inspired each person and filled them with fresh courage.

SHIN'ICHI AND HIS party arrived in New York on May 17. It was his fourth visit to this city. On the 18th, he attended a meeting at the New York Community Center. Having heard from the American leaders that the number of youthful members was increasing here as well and that they were developing their lives, Shin'ichi had been looking forward to meeting with them.

As he was leaving his hotel to go to the meeting, Shin'ichi came across a Japanese youth standing by the entrance. A local leader introduced the young man, saying: "This is Yukihiko Sasahara, and he's a dancer by profession. He asked to be a part of the security team during your visit, so he is working in that capacity."

"I see. Thank you very much!" Shin'ichi replied.

A somewhat nervous Sasahara began to introduce himself: "My name is Sasahara. I'm very pleased to meet you. I started practicing last year and currently am doing my best in activities so that I can learn more about the Soka Gakkai and about Nichiren Buddhism."

Sasahara had thick, prominent eyebrows and distinguished facial features. At the same time, there was something about his expression that betrayed worry. He seemed to be troubled.

Sensing that he might be facing problems in his career as a dancer, Shin'ichi said: "Youth is a time of struggle. But no matter what difficulties you encounter, if you carry through with faith, you can use everything to your advantage and your hardships will become your greatest assets in life. Faith is the supreme path that causes our lives to shine brilliantly. The important thing is to make kosen-rufu your mission in life and to keep moving forward to the very end."

"I understand!" Sasahara replied energetically, his eyes brightening.

The fact was that Sasahara had been struggling about the decision of whether or not to continue dancing.

Sasahara had first thought of becoming a dancer when he was in his second year of high school. He happened to see an American musical at the movies and it had captured his imagination. When he shared his ambition with his parents, they were staunchly opposed to it. But the more they tried to dissuade him, the more convinced he became.

BEFORE LONG, Yukihiko Sasahara's parents caved in to their son's single-minded will and supported his decision to become a dancer. After graduating from high school, he entered college and pursued drama. He thought this would aid him in achieving his goal of dancing in musicals.

However, in his second year of studies, his father developed stomach cancer and died. Finding himself in financial straits, he had no choice but to withdraw from school. But rather than deter him from his goal, these circumstances strengthened his resolve to make it as a dancer.

While working part time as a janitor and at other odd jobs, Sasahara began taking dance classes and applying himself in earnest to learning jazz. Eventually, his efforts bore fruit and he was accepted into a ballet company formed by a renowned artist and his protégés. The range of his opportunities expanded gradually, and soon he was appearing on television.

Around this time, Sasahara's younger sister, who had married and moved to San Francisco, was pressing him to join her in the United States. New York's Broadway was of course the mecca of musicals. Thinking of this, Sasahara's dream grew bigger, but as he didn't have the funds to make such a move, he hesitated in coming to a decision. Finally deciding that he would regret it forever if he didn't go, he somehow managed to scrape together the money and set sail to the United States in March 1964. He was twenty-eight years old. When he arrived in the United States, Sasahara stayed with his sister for a week before heading to New York.

Encompassing the area around Times Square, the Broadway theater district drew dancers, actors and singers from around the world. The streets, lit up by neon signs, were bustling with activity late into the night; indeed, it was a sleepless city. Intermingled with the blinking neon lights were the joy and despair of those who dreamed of stardom.

Quite often musicals that succeeded on Broadway would become hits in other parts of the United States as well as overseas. Such well-known musicals as *The King and I* and *West Side Story* first debuted on Broadway before becoming worldwide sensations.

IT WASN'T UNCOMMON for unknown dancers, actors or singers to become a world sensation overnight if the Broadway production they starred in was a major hit. This meant that there was fierce competition among performers and that the rise and fall of stars on Broadway was dramatic.

Sasahara began taking dance lessons while working as a dishwasher in a restaurant. He was living in a tiny one-room apartment with a shared bath and toilet. Life in the United States, where he couldn't even speak the language, was harder than he had originally imagined.

Needless to say, the standards of dance in America were very high, and Sasahara sensed there were huge hurdles he would have to overcome. But this fueled his fighting spirit, spurring him to put forth greater effort than others. As a result, he won the praise of a top dancer who complimented his unique dancing style. However, while technically he could dance with the best of them, his Japanese physique set him at a disadvantage. He tried to compensate for this by polishing his technical ability, but he just couldn't seem to get a role. Before long, insecurity and anxiety started to creep into his heart.

It was about this time that a Japanese-American co-worker at the restaurant told him about Nichiren Buddhism, and Sasahara attended his first Soka Gakkai discussion meeting. Moved by everyone's passion and sincerity, he decided to join. This was in February 1966. He was hesitant, however, to get involved in Gakkai activities.

In August that same year, a cultural event sponsored by the Min-On Concert Association, incorporating singing, music and dance performances, was scheduled to be held in conjunction with the All-America General Meeting in New York. When Sasahara was asked to perform, he jumped at the chance. He was overjoyed by the prospect of dancing on stage.

Learning that more dancers were needed, Sasahara approached a young man named Takafumi Kuriyama, whom he knew through dancing. When Kuriyama heard that the event was to be sponsored by the Soka Gakkai-founded Min-On Concert Association, he revealed that he had also joined the Soka Gakkai in 1960 back in Japan.

ALTHOUGH KURIYAMA had become a Soka Gakkai member, he felt restricted by the organization and had therefore always declined invitations to attend meetings or other activities while he was in Japan. So when he heard about the Min-On event from Sasahara, he agreed to participate so long as he only had to perform.

Kuriyama had also been inspired to become a dancer after seeing an American musical on the silver screen. He dropped out of high school and began taking classes at a performing arts school, later joining the prestigious Nichigeki Dance Company in Tokyo. He gradually made a name for himself, and was even referred to in the Japanese press as a "rising star." However, deeply affected by the captivating dance style of an American performer on tour in Japan, he decided to go and study in New York, the birthplace of musicals. Thus, in June 1964, the twenty-five-year-old Kuriyama moved to the United States.

Like Sasahara, Kuriyama's life in America was difficult as he struggled to take dance lessons in between part-time jobs. Also, he had recently been diagnosed with an ulcer, brought on perhaps by his stressful lifestyle. It was then that Sasahara invited Kuriyama to perform in the Min-On event. The two had originally met through the dance world in Japan and, brought together again by their common nationality, their friendship continued to develop in New York.

As Kuriyama and Sasahara became increasingly involved in preparations for the show, they began to interact more with other Soka Gakkai members and eventually started to attend young men's gatherings and discussion meetings. Both were astonished to find that, contrary to what they had imagined, the Soka Gakkai was not a rigid organization, but one filled with cheer, hope and friendship. At these activities they discovered the warmth and brilliance of people dedicated to working not only for their personal happiness but also that of others.

As the two young men continued to chant, they felt a powerful stirring in their lives, and gradually their conviction in Nichiren Buddhism deepened. By the time the Min-On event was over, both Kuriyama and Sasahara were joyfully and enthusiastically engaging in Soka Gakkai activities. Even Kuriyama's ulcer had healed, without him realizing it.

They were particularly inspired by President Yamamoto's guidance that kosen-rufu is the creation of a new culture of humanism.

SASAHARA AND Kuriyama also put great energy into sharing Buddhist philosophy with fellow dancers and musicians, one after another.

Around this time, the United States' involvement in the Vietnam War was increasing and there was a mounting fear among young people of being drafted for military service. In addition, antiwar protests were springing up all over the country.

Within this social context were a growing number of youth referred to as "hippies," who rejected established social institutions, mores and values, and sought personal fulfillment. Many sported long hair and wore eccentric clothing, and some used marijuana regularly. Many of them were musicians.

It was this group in particular that Sasahara and Kuriyama targeted in their propagation efforts. They said: "The war in Vietnam is wrong, and there are a lot of problems in American society today. But to drop out of society and seek only personal fulfillment ultimately amounts to nothing more than egoism or escapism. True happiness cannot be found this way.

"What's important is to continue struggling within the realities of society, rather than running away. By developing a strong self that is never defeated and endeavoring to change society for the better, we can create happiness both for ourselves and others. Nichiren Daishonin's Buddhism teaches how to do this."

Sasahara and Kuriyama spoke with conviction about the Buddhist principle that a transformation in the life of a single individual can lead to a change in the destiny of a nation. A steady stream of these youth who had given up on society began to practice. Many others would later follow suit, and through faith, discover life's true meaning and savor genuine happiness.

It was a dramatic shift from "hippy to happy"—a shift that characterized the Soka Gakkai in the United States at that time.

Meanwhile, Sasahara and Kuriyama continued to strive hard in their dance careers. Various jobs started coming in, among them work in children's theater. They were also able to get some auditions, although they were still unsuccessful in landing a role.

O NE DAY, Sasahara and Kuriyama both auditioned for a musical that called for Asian performers. When they were given the roles, they hugged each other from sheer joy.

However, an American dancer complained to the director, saying: "This is America. Why do we have to use Asians? In terms of rhythm or power of expression, we would do a much better job."

"I hear you," replied the director, "but this musical calls for an Asian cast."

"That's not a problem. With some makeup, we can become Asian too!"

Everything was fair play when it came to capturing a role. Brutal competition for survival was also part of the reality of Broadway. In the end, the director hired American dancers.

That night, Sasahara and Kuriyama wandered the streets of Broadway utterly dejected and overwhelmed with frustration. They trembled with anger under the stinging glare of the bright neon lights, tears filling their eyes.

After this, they continued to audition for parts, but could not land a role in a real Broadway musical. By this time, Sasahara was already over thirty years old, and he was beginning to feel his physical limitations. He thought of returning to Japan, but at the same time he didn't want to leave without having succeeded as a dancer. So he remained in the United States in this state of uncertainty.

It was around this time that Sasahara met Shin'ichi Yamamoto at the hotel in New York. Shin'ichi's encouragement that he should make kosen-rufu his mission and continue moving forward had left a deep impression on him. As he engaged in Soka Gakkai activities, he began to think of kosen-rufu in the United States as his personal goal in life.

He chanted in earnest, praying about how he should proceed. As he did so, a picture of the vast stage of American kosen-rufu began to unfold in his mind's eye, and he started to feel that his mission lay in achieving that goal. Excitement filled his being. Compared to the grand stage of kosen-rufu, the Broadway stage seemed insignificant.

SASAHARA BECAME increasingly convinced that the reason he had moved to the United States was in fact so that he could work for kosen-rufu there.

After chanting abundantly, he decided to give up dancing. But he did not return to Japan. Rather, he resolved to devote the rest of his life to realizing the spread of Nichiren's teachings throughout America. He thus began looking for employment so that he could secure a stable income. And in 1968, he was hired by an airline company.

Everyone has their own unique path in life, and there are many ways to live. But no matter what path we follow, if we dedicate ourselves to the great mission of kosen-rufu, we are sure to bring out our highest potential and lead a victorious life.

The Mystic Law is a teaching that enables us to make the most of every experience. In other words, nothing is wasted. Buddhism expounds the infallible formula that when we exert ourselves for kosen-rufu, all of our hopes and dreams will be fulfilled.

After leaving his dancing career, Sasahara made a personal vow to support the many other talented dancers and artists who had begun practicing Buddhism. He wanted to help them achieve what he couldn't. He felt that this was the way for him to contribute to kosen-rufu—to the creation of a new humanistic culture.

He helped dancers and musicians understand the principles of Buddhism, warmly listening to their struggles and encouraging them sincerely. He was determined to become a source of support for their growth.

In this way, the tradition of fostering performing artists became part of the Soka Gakkai's legacy in the United States. Over time, such world-renowned jazz musicians as bassist Buster Williams, pianist Herbie Hancock and saxophonist Wayne Shorter became active members.

Later, Sasahara joined the staff of the Soka Gakkai organization in America and dedicated himself to working for the members. As for Kuriyama, despite the many twists and turns that took him temporarily to different fields of work, he continued in the world of dance. He eventually moved on to designing and producing musicals, as well as establishing a dance school in Japan.

IN THE CAR on the way to the New York Community Center, Shin'ichi asked one of the local leaders: "Are there many artists among the members here?"

"There are," the leader replied. "One of them, a young women's member, is a flutist. And our local young women's leader, Fujie Onozawa, is skilled in the art of making traditional Japanese dolls. Since Fujie took on her leadership responsibilities two years ago, the young women's division has really begun to expand. While petite in stature, she has a strong fighting spirit and gives her all to every endeavor. She also takes very good care of others."

"I am reassured to hear that the youth are developing in New York as well," Shin'ichi said. "No matter how dynamic and solid an organization appears to be, if its youth are not growing, it will eventually stagnate. Fostering young people is crucial to the achievement of kosen-rufu."

"What is the key to raising young people?" the leader then asked.

Shin'ichi's response came without hesitation: "We must trust and respect youth. It is wrong to treat them as subordinate simply because they haven't been practicing for very long, or because they're younger. We need be firmly determined to support them in becoming even more capable than ourselves, empowering them to fully develop their potential.

"In addition, we need to help them gain a thorough understanding of the basic thinking and behavior of a leader of kosen-rufu. The only way to really do this is through experience. Theoretical comprehension and practical application are two very separate things.

"For example, simply being cognizant of the necessity for swift, effective action in the event of an earthquake or fire does not mean that we will actually do what's required when the time comes. We need actual, hands-on training.

"The same could be said of our Buddhist practice. I recently heard that members of the young men's Traffic Control Group (forerunner of the Soka Group) are being highly praised at work. I am sure this is due to their training. They energetically greet their co-workers at the start of the day, are always punctual, have a strong sense of responsibility and take the initiative. This has earned them the trust of others.

"Nichiren Daishonin writes: 'Iron, when heated in flames and pounded, becomes a fine sword' (WND, 303. Thus, it is important that youth actively seek out their own training.

"FURTHERMORE, in fostering youth we need to entrust them with specific assignments and give them opportunities to take the lead. It is by taking responsibility and accumulating experience that people develop their talents. If we don't provide youth with opportunities to challenge themselves, they will never grow.

"We may, however, feel compelled to step in or take over, thinking that it would be easier or more expeditious to do things ourselves rather than leave it to inexperienced youth. But leaders need to have the magnanimity to take full responsibility even if the youth make mistakes."

The leader who had asked the question gave a wry smile of acknowledgment.

"At the same time," Shin'ichi continued, "if we simply tell the youth to do this or that without guiding them, it's as if we're waiting for them to fail. First, we ourselves have to take action and set an example, and then we can give them the responsibility, encouraging them all the while.

"Of course, it's important to bring any problems to their attention, as well as to set new targets for them. Above all else, however, we must give them hope and the confidence that they can definitely succeed if they put their minds to it."

Shin'ichi gave his all to elucidating the essential points for fostering youth.

"Another crucial point is that youth is a time of facing various struggles, a time when people start to think about the future and things like getting married. When burdened with worries, people cannot freely display their abilities. We therefore need to carefully listen to the youth, discuss their problems with them and inspire them to use their hardships as a springboard for deepening their faith.

"If, for example, someone is struggling with difficult human relations in the workplace, we should encourage him or her to engage in Soka Gakkai activities with the goal of resolving these problems.

"If we liken our advancement toward the great goal of kosen-rufu to the earth revolving around the sun, then our efforts to solve our personal problems and actualize our prayers are like the earth turning on its axis. The combination of these two motions opens the path of happiness before us.

"At any rate, what matters is that we look after the youth as if they were our younger siblings. Young people will not develop in an organization that is cold and heartless."

BEFORE LONG, Shin'ichi and the others reached the New York Community Center, where thirty or so representative members had gathered. This center had been established four years earlier as the base of activities for the entire eastern region, but since it consisted of only two rented rooms on the first floor of the building, it could not accommodate many people. Out of consideration for their neighbors, the members used extreme care when holding activities, including chanting as quietly as possible.

When Shin'ichi visited this community center during his visit to North and South America in March the previous year, it pained him to see the members having to be so inhibited. He wanted them to have a spacious and splendid center that they could use freely without worries. Since then, he had been discussing plans for establishing a new center with senior leaders of the American organization.

On his first visit to New York seven years earlier, there were only a dozen or so participants, including guests, at the discussion meeting he attended. But now, that small group had grown into a joint chapter encompassing New York City and the surrounding region, and the community center had become too small. Shin'ichi was deeply grateful for the members' strenuous efforts.

After reciting the sutra and chanting Nam-myoho-renge-kyo, Shin'ichi expressed his sincere gratitude to the members, saying: "All of you have been striving diligently to open the way for kosen-rufu to spread not only in New York, but also throughout the entire United States. Thank you so much. I would like to convey my profound appreciation for your dedicated efforts."

He then bowed deeply.

The appreciation and sincerity of a leader strikes a resonant chord in the hearts of members and weaves a beautiful tapestry of unity.

Seeing Shin'ichi's sincere gesture, several Japanese-

American women's members covered their faces with their hands and wept in emotion. These women were pioneers of kosen-rufu in America who had traveled across New York and the rest of the eastern part of the country to share Buddhism with others.

Following Shin'ichi's guidance, each of them had obtained a driver's license and had driven far and wide spreading Nichiren's teachings. Their visits took them to places that reached below fourteen degrees Fahrenheit in the middle of winter. There were times when the fog was so dense that they had to pull over and wait until it cleared before they could move on. And there were other times when they just wanted to burst into tears, such as when their car broke down, and they were left stranded in the middle of the night.

THE HEARTS of these dedicated pioneers were filled with memories of having surmounted numerous difficulties. In their efforts to share Buddhism with other Americans in their broken English, some of them had been yelled at and called derogatory names. Although World War II was over, hatred toward the Japanese still persisted.

Nevertheless, they persevered, telling each other that it was only natural for them to encounter hardships and sufferings along the path to achieving the noble goal of kosen-rufu. Realizing now that President Yamamoto had always understood their struggles, they were overcome with joy and emotion. Indeed, those who have endured suffering are deeply touched by the warm concern of others.

The more we dedicate ourselves to our Soka Gakkai activities, the more we can polish our lives, transform our karma, accumulate good fortune and become happy. These activities constitute our inalienable right as human beings, and they must be protected at all costs.

After he spoke, Shin'ichi went around the room and shook hands with each of the participants. As he did so, he came across a familiar face—it was Teruko Izumiya, the sole person to welcome him in Toronto, Canada, when he went there seven years earlier. At that time, Izumiya was not yet practicing, but at the insistence of her mother, a Soka Gakkai member back in Japan, she had gone to the airport to meet Shin'ichi.

Izumiya started practicing nineteen months later. Perhaps due to stress from her life in Canada, to which she was not accustomed, she had begun suffering from allergies. It was then that she remembered the words that Shin'ichi had shared with her during their encounter at the airport: "If anything should happen, chant Nam-myoho-renge-kyo." Meanwhile, her mother, worried about her illness, had also written to her from Tokyo to encourage her to embrace Nichiren Buddhism. Motivated by a strong desire to regain her health, Izumiya decided to give the practice a try.

At first she was skeptical, but in her earnest efforts to chant every day, her health improved. Before long, she had completely recovered, and this gave her confidence in the power of faith.

WHEN IZUMIYA accompanied her husband on a business trip to Japan in November 1964, she went to see Shin'ichi at the Soka Gakkai Headquarters.

She was convinced that President Yamamoto would not remember her at all. But as soon as he saw her, Shin'ichi said with great deference, "Thank you so much for kindly welcoming me in Toronto."

Overjoyed to learn that she had begun practicing, he added: "There is no life more noble, happy or fulfilling than one devoted to spreading Nichiren's Buddhism. I am counting on you to realize kosen-rufu in Canada."

"I will do my best!" she replied without hesitation.

This was the moment that Izumiya awakened to her great mission of Canadian kosen-rufu. From that point on, her endeavors toward that goal began.

Now, two-and-a-half years later, Izumiya, who had developed her life tremendously, had driven more than ten hours from Toronto to meet Shin'ichi in New York. Brimming with excitement, Izumiya announced to Shin'ichi: "I came here today with three other members. The membership in Canada is also steadily growing."

"That's wonderful," Shin'ichi replied. "I am really happy to see you working so hard."

Praising her efforts, he firmly shook her hand. The seed of encouragement that he had planted seven years earlier had begun to blossom magnificently.

If seeds are not planted, nothing will grow. That is why, for the sake of the future, seeds of hope must be sown through dialogue now. It is only through our endeavors today that the fruits of tomorrow are born.

After shaking hands with everyone, Shin'ichi said to them: "Since the membership in New York is growing and the community center is becoming too small, I'd like to establish a larger center here. What do you think?"

The room erupted in thunderous applause. Once again, a new goal for advancement was set.

After the meeting, Shin'ichi escorted High Priest Nittatsu on a tour of the United Nations Headquarters, the Empire State Building and other sights.

By afternoon the following day, May 19, Shin'ichi and his party had departed from John F. Kennedy International Airport and were flying over the Atlantic Ocean toward their next destination—Paris, France.

SHORTLY BEFORE ten o'clock in the evening on May 19, Shin'ichi Yamamoto and his party arrived in Paris.

"President Yamamoto!" When they entered the airport lobby, they were greeted by Europe No. 1 Headquarters Leader Eiji Kawasaki, who stood smiling brightly in his suit and characteristic bow tie. Next to him was Shotaro Hasebe, an artist who had been appointed as the Paris Chapter leader in August the year before.

Shaking hands with Kawasaki, Shin'ichi asked: "Do you still have pain?"

"It's almost completely gone," Kawasaki responded.

"I'm glad to hear that. You look healthier and more vibrant than when I last saw you in Japan."

"Since receiving guidance from you at the Soka Gakkai Headquarters then," Kawasaki remarked, "my wife and I feel as if we've been given a new lease on life and we have been working hard together. In addition, my physical condition has improved immensely."

Shin'ichi's wife, Mineko, who was standing nearby, said: "You know, from the moment my husband heard that you and your wife had been in a car accident and were in the hospital, he has been praying for you every day."

"I don't know what to say. I'm deeply grateful," Kawasaki replied.

In April of the preceding year, 1966, the Kawasakis had been seriously injured in a car accident and were in the hospital for more than six months.

On that fateful day, they were on their way by car to encourage a member in Poitiers, about 190 miles outside Paris. Eiji was at the wheel. It had taken them a while to find the house, and so it was already quite late by the time they started driving back. They had not yet eaten dinner, but since the next day was the beginning of the work-week, they wanted to get home as soon as possible. Along the way, it started raining.

Around one in the morning, they stopped to fill up their car at a gas station in Orleans, the city where Joan of Arc, the "Maid of Orleans," saved France by pushing back the English army during the Hundred Years' War. They rested for a moment, but seeing that the rain had stopped, they quickly set out again. Eiji told his wife to go ahead and sleep, and before long Yoshie was dozing off in the passenger seat. Realizing that they were two-thirds of the way there, he relaxed a little. But soon he became overpowered by extreme fatigue and started to fall asleep at the wheel.

THE NEXT INSTANT, through a drowsy haze, Eiji saw he had swerved off the road and was hurtling toward a large sycamore tree, which was illuminated by his headlights.

He slammed on the brakes, but it was too late. The Kawasakis' car hit the tree head-on, shattering the windshield. Eiji barely regained consciousness. Having closed his eyes from the force of the violent impact, he slowly opened them again. The moon was shining brightly in the sky, which was now cleared of rain. As he looked out at smoke rising from the hood, he thought he saw the face of Shin'ichi gazing back at him.

"Sensei . . . ," he said to himself.

Immediately, he was seized by a powerful sensation: "I will not die here!" he vowed.

Strangely, he felt no pain. Looking over to the passenger seat, he saw his wife lying unconscious, her upper body ejected through the windshield. He tried to call out her name, but no sound came out. He reached over with his right hand and shook her, but she didn't respond. Fearing the worst, he tried to inch closer to her but his right leg would not move. It was trapped by the engine, which had shot through to the driver's seat and was almost crushing his leg. Fragments of glass were also embedded in his cheeks.

Eiji had no notion of how much time had elapsed before he heard the distant sound of an ambulance siren. Someone in a passing car had seen the accident and called for help.

The Kawasakis were transported to a hospital in Orleans. The femur in Eiji's right leg was broken, and the kneecap shattered. Yoshie also sustained severe injuries, with compound fractures of the femur and tibia.

Accidents are always foreshadowed. Eiji Kawasaki had been involved in an accident once before when he had lost control of his car while driving in the rain, hit a boulder and overturned. There had been no casualties, but the car had been totaled.

WHILE VISITING JAPAN shortly after his first accident, Eiji reported the incident to Shin'ichi Yamamoto, who said: "You should take this as a warning of an even more serious accident. Leaders need to be ever vigilant, perceiving an accident as a warning and taking appropriate measures to ensure it doesn't happen again. By doing so, critical situations can be avoided.

"From now on, I hope you will chant earnestly with the determination never to have another accident, and that you will drive safely, observing all the rules of the road.

"Moreover, as exhaustion or lack of sleep can be a major cause of accidents, it's important to make sure to drive only in the best physical condition. That is the duty of a driver. When you haven't slept much, it might be best to have someone else drive, or to take the train or bus, even though it may be less convenient.

"When you have to cover long distances, it's a good idea to stop regularly to rest, so as not to get overly tired. And if you are feeling drowsy, I suggest chewing gum or finding some other method to keep yourself awake. It's also important that you don't become so engrossed in conversation with a passenger that you are distracted from what you are doing.

"Leaders should not only take these precautions themselves, but also remind members to drive home safely after meetings or other activities. This simple gesture will put everyone on alert and help prevent accidents."

Nichiren Daishonin warmly cautioned his disciple Shijo Kingo on a regular basis with such words as: "As I have said before, be millions of times more careful than ever" (WND, 839), and "Make sure that you ride a good horse" (WND, 953). Shin'ichi's guidance was likewise very clear and concrete.

Placing a hand on Kawasaki's shoulder, Shin'ichi continued: "Mr. Kawasaki, I hope you will buy a larger car this time, one that is solidly built. If you have an accident, all your efforts will have been for naught. Not only will you and your family suffer, but it will cause members to worry as well. I never want to see any of my precious fellow members injured or killed in an accident."

EIJI KAWASAKI vowed to take Shin'ichi's advice to heart, and he did indeed strive to put it into practice. He even bought a large car.

However, his trip to Poitiers happened to come after a few consecutive nights of little sleep. He had also been on the go since early in the morning that day, giving personal guidance and talking to people about Buddhism, and his fatigue was mounting. He knew that under such circumstances, he should not drive, but in this case it was definitely more convenient to go by car.

Today, it cannot be helped. I'll just chant and drive with extreme caution. With this thought, he set out on the long journey, despite his exhaustion.

In any situation, it is a grave mistake to neglect basic common sense and assume that we will be protected just because we have faith or because we chant. There is no mindset more dangerous than this. One might say that this way of thinking in itself is a manifestation of devilish functions.

Nichiren states: "Trifling matters accumulate to become grave ones" (WND, 1133). Any one of the factors contributing to a major accident may seem of little consequence at first glance. But small errors or oversights provide an opening for devilish functions to take advantage and cause irrevocable damage. That is why ostensibly minor incidents need to be taken seriously.

One could say that the Kawasakis' accident had been caused by a mere moment of neglect.

Eiji Kawasaki lost consciousness as he was being taken to the hospital by ambulance. When he eventually came to in the hospital room, the first thought that entered his mind was whether his wife was still alive. He asked the nurse, who replied in French: "She has suffered severe injuries, but her life is no longer in danger. She's now sleeping in another room."

Eiji's eyes filled with tears as he thought: *We were protected! We were protected by the Gohonzon!* He then gave the nurse the telephone number of Shotaro Hasebe, and asked her to contact him.

When Hasebe arrived at the hospital the next morning, Kawasaki requested that he inform President Yamamoto of the accident. Hasebe immediately sent a telegram to the Soka Gakkai Headquarters in Tokyo.

SHIN'ICHI YAMAMOTO was shocked when he read the telegram from Hasebe. While greatly relieved to learn that the Kawasakis had survived the accident, he was deeply concerned about whether they would make a complete physical recovery.

Since Eisuke Akizuki was scheduled to go to Paris on official Soka Gakkai business, Shin'ichi asked him to visit the Kawasakis in the hospital. When Akizuki arrived, he found them both hospitalized in the same room, their legs in casts and kept immobile. Handing them gifts from Shin'ichi, he said: "President Yamamoto asked me to convey this message to you: 'Your lives were protected because you have persevered in faith. Through this accident, you have expiated negative karma and lessened your karmic retribution.'"

To "lessen karmic retribution" refers to the Buddhist principle of transforming past negative causes through the beneficial power of Buddhist practice and experiencing them in a lesser form in this lifetime.

Akizuki continued relaying Shin'ichi's message: "President Yamamoto further remarked that had you been even more seriously dedicated to your practice, this accident may have been avoided altogether."

These words struck Eiji Kawasaki profoundly. Holding a doctoral degree in medicine, he had been a researcher at the highly acclaimed research and education institution Collége de France. But he had resigned from his post the year before when the professor with whom he was doing joint research went back to America, and it became too difficult for him to continue alone. Since then, his colleague had repeatedly invited him to come to the United States so that they could carry on their work.

Kawasaki didn't know what to do. Realizing that President Yamamoto had entrusted him with kosen-rufu in Europe, he strongly felt that he could not leave the country. After carefully considering the matter, he decided to give up the research and remain in France. He was then hired as a Soka Gakkai staff member and embarked on a new course.

However, having worked as a researcher for so many years, he had a hard time letting go of his previous profession. There were often times when he found himself subconsciously walking toward the College de France when he was supposed to be heading to a discussion meeting, or thinking about some research topic while a meeting was taking place.

KAWASAKI FULLY INTENDED to dedicate himself to serving the members as a Soka Gakkai staff member for the sake of kosen-rufu. But somehow he could not forget his previous career and was therefore not wholly committed to the task. This hesitation prevented him from giving his all to fulfilling his mission.

It is easy to receive small benefits from practicing Nichiren's Buddhism. But producing the great benefit of changing karma is another matter. This is because it is not possible to change our karma unless we deeply examine the true nature of our mind and character—which has shaped our destiny—and then work to polish our life and achieve our human revolution. Toward this end, we need to devote ourselves wholeheartedly to carrying out our mission for kosen-rufu—an endeavor that requires chanting Nam-myoho-renge-kyo with resolute faith, challenging obstacles and striving to do away with injustice.

Strictly speaking, it could be said that Eiji Kawasaki had not given himself entirely to working for kosen-rufu. The slight hesitation in his inner determination was a hindrance to his own great development, which meant he could not fully surmount the enormous barrier that was his karma.

Hearing Shin'ichi Yamamoto's message through Eisuke Akizuki, Kawasaki felt as if everything suddenly fell into perspective. He said: "I truly understand what President Yamamoto is telling me. I was practicing halfheartedly. I have much to reflect upon. Please convey to President Yamamoto how sorry I am to have caused him to worry. I will get better as soon as possible and work for kosen-rufu with a completely renewed determination.'"

Later, Yoshie and Eiji Kawasaki both underwent surgery and had metal pins placed in their legs to support their femur bones, an operation that required them both to undergo large blood transfusions.

When Eiji was being discharged from the hospital in October 1966, six months after the accident, he had a talk with his wife: "Because of our blood transfusions, French blood now flows in our veins. I therefore feel that from now on it is our duty to work for the happiness of the people of France, as well as for the sake of peace in all of Europe."

"I agree," Yoshie replied. "I'll be in the hospital for a little while longer, but as soon as I get out, I will also do my absolute best."

THE KAWASAKIS turned their accident into an
opportunity to make a profound determination to
dedicate their lives to the achievement of kosen-rufu in
France and the rest of Europe.

As if to make up for the six months during which he
was bedridden, Eiji Kawasaki plunged himself energetically into Soka Gakkai activities. He first set out to visit
all the members and encourage them personally. He
knew that life-to-life dialogue could inspire fresh resolve
in people more effectively than any large meeting.

Although he was out of the hospital, he still experienced pain in his leg. Since many of the apartment buildings in Paris had no elevators, he sometimes had to climb
four or five flights of stairs, painfully taking one step at a
time while dragging his aching limb behind. Making frequent stops on his way up, he would crouch down to ease
the pain and catch his breath, his forehead covered in

sweat. But he gritted his teeth and continued his ascent, determined to meet with his fellow members and encourage them with all his might.

Delighted to see Kawasaki's recovery, the members hugged him and shed tears of joy. Even those who had not fully embraced the practice would listen attentively to his experience and be inspired to make a stronger commitment.

Yoshie was discharged from the hospital the following spring, in 1967. As soon as she could walk without the aid of crutches, the couple left for Japan, eager to meet Shin'ichi Yamamoto and express their gratitude to him in person.

Meanwhile, having received news of their visit, Shin'-ichi's heart leapt. He repeatedly remarked to his wife, Mineko, how happy he was at their recovery.

But when the Kawasakis arrived at the Soka Gakkai Headquarters, they were met by Shin'ichi's strict reprimands: "How could you have caused an accident at such a critical time!"

The Kawasakis' smiling faces suddenly stiffened. They had been expecting some words of sympathy. In actuality, Shin'ichi wanted to extend such words to them, but the Kawasakis were leaders who shouldered the responsibility for kosen-rufu in Europe.

"IT IS INEXCUSABLE that Soka Gakkai leaders should have caused a car accident!" Shin'ichi Yamamoto scolded. "You have made everyone worry and hindered the progress of kosen-rufu!"

Shin'ichi wanted to drive home to the Kawasakis just

how serious a responsibility being a leader of kosen-rufu is.

His words pierced Eiji and Yoshie Kawasaki's hearts. "We are very sorry for the trouble we have caused!" they said, tears filling their eyes as they deeply bowed their heads.

"If you understand what I'm saying, that's what counts," Shin'ichi continued in a milder tone. "Leaders of kosen-rufu are responsible for the happiness of their fellow members. The writings of Nichiren Daishonin elucidate that the greater responsibility you take on for kosen-rufu, the more forcefully you will be assailed by devilish functions. But you mustn't give them the slightest edge nor ever be defeated by them. If you are unable to carry out your duties as top leaders, it is the members who will suffer. The reason I'm speaking to you so strictly is because I absolutely do not want you to have another accident."

With a smile, he added: "I am truly happy to see that you have both recovered. I was really worried. I'll be going to Europe after the May 3 Headquarters General Meeting. Let's make a fresh start together."

The genuine joy in Shin'ichi's voice conveyed to the Kawasakis just how concerned he had been about their conditions.

Immediately after attending the Headquarters general meeting, which commemorated the seventh anniversary of Shin'ichi's inauguration as president, the Kawasakis returned to France to commence preparations for welcoming Shin'ichi and his delegation.

Now, at the airport in Paris, Shin'ichi Yamamoto firmly

grasped the hand of Eiji Kawasaki, who had come to meet him, and said: "The Soka Gakkai in Japan has entered the second stage of its endeavors for kosen-rufu, and is advancing with great hope. It's time for the organization in Europe to do the same, setting out boldly into the future."

"I understand," Kawasaki replied. "With the determination to repay my debt of gratitude, I will continue to press forward as long as I live!" His face shone with fighting spirit.

THE FOLLOWING DAY, May 20, was blessed with fine weather. On this day, Shin'ichi participated in a Gohonzon-enshrinement ceremony at the Paris Community Center, located in the Paris suburb of Neuilly. The center was an elegant two-story building situated on a plot of land about 7,100 square feet in area.

Until the establishment of this center, Eiji Kawasaki's apartment had served as both the Europe Headquarters administrative office as well as a meeting place for members. But with only two rooms, it could accommodate no more than twenty people. In addition, every time they held a meeting, the neighbors would complain. The new building was therefore the perfect size.

Approximately 150 members from France, the United Kingdom, West Germany, the Netherlands, Sweden and other European countries had joyfully gathered for the enshrinement ceremony. After reciting the sutra and chanting Nam-myoho-renge-kyo, several of the leaders from Japan delivered greetings.

Shin'ichi spoke next, saying: "The great river of kosen-rufu began with just one person—Nichiren Daishonin. Likewise, the Soka Gakkai started with President Makiguchi and President Toda. But today, our organization has expanded into the world. Though the organization in Europe is still small with only eight hundred or so member-households, according to this same principle, in ten or twenty years, you are certain to see tremendous growth. This, however, means that each of you must strive with a stand-alone spirit, without being dependent on each other. Everything rests on how many people summon forth lion-like courage and forge ahead with the resolve that they will realize kosen-rufu, even if they have to do it alone, and be victorious without fail.

"The accumulation of each person's determination and each person's triumph leads to great victory. It thus follows that ushering in a new era and creating history are not extraordinary feats. They simply require that each person challenge his or her own personal objectives, and win on a daily basis. It all comes down to what action we are taking right now.

"I hope that you will awaken to your role as protagonists of kosen-rufu and enact a bold drama of surmounting difficulties on the grand stage of life as champions of faith."

The members applauded vigorously in an expression of their fresh resolve.

Also announced at the meeting was the formation of Montparnasse Chapter, the third Soka Gakkai chapter in France, and London Chapter, the first to be established in the United Kingdom.

WHEN SHIN'ICHI finished speaking, he and the other members went outside and planted a cypress tree in the garden of the community center to mark the occasion. They then divided into several groups for commemorative photographs with Shin'ichi. The whole time, Shin'ichi continued to talk with different members.

The first person he spoke to was Shotaro Hasebe, the leader of Paris Chapter. "Mr. Hasebe, thank you so much for your tremendous efforts," Shin'ichi said as he patted him on the shoulder. "Because you stood up and took responsibility, the organization here in France was protected."

When the Kawasakis were hospitalized after their accident, Hasebe had decided it was up to him to carry on in their place and thus set out in earnest to encourage the members. He had taken great pains to ensure that no one became discouraged by the Kawasakis' situation or began to harbor doubts about Buddhism.

Hasebe had told himself: "If anyone should stop practicing at this point, it will be my personal failure. I want to welcome President Yamamoto to Paris with every single member having deepened their faith!" Filled with such intense resolve, he had striven each day to support the temporarily leaderless French organization.

Seeing the activities in France steadily expanding despite the Kawasakis' absence, Shin'ichi knew that there must be someone fighting hard behind the scenes. When he learned that this person was Hasebe, he looked forward to having the opportunity to praise and acknowledge his efforts.

Tears welled up in Hasebe's eyes as he listened to Shin'ichi's words. He was overjoyed that President Yamamoto had been observing his quiet endeavors.

Shin'ichi then turned his gaze to the other members present. Several young women's members of Japanese descent bowed to him, their cheeks pink with excitement.

"I see that the number of young women's members has really grown in France as well," Shin'ichi said to them. "The young women's division is really important. As long as your warm smiles are present, the Soka Gakkai in France will eternally develop. Please advance dynamically, in friendship and high spirits, aiming toward the twenty-first century."

When he said this, a young woman with a childlike face called out loudly, "I will!" Her name was Sadae Murano, and she was a young women's member who had moved to France from Saga Prefecture in Japan six months earlier.

TWO YEARS EARLIER, in late 1965, Murano attended a young women's meeting in her native Saga Prefecture. On that occasion, a leader talked about Masayo Mizusawa, a young woman's member who had just returned to Japan from France.

The leader related: "Ms. Mizusawa went to France to study hairstyling and joined the Soka Gakkai there. Although she could not attend today's meeting, she will be in town for a while. She is determined to return to France and to devote her life to working for kosen-rufu.

"From now on, the world is our stage. The time has come for us, the members of the young women's division, to spread our wings and take flight into the vast world."

Murano was deeply impressed by the fact that a young woman from the same prefecture was moving to France to work for kosen-rufu. She had graduated from high school that spring but was struggling to find direction in her life. Having practiced Buddhism from an early age together with her family, she had always wanted to dedicate herself to kosen-rufu and to contribute to the realization of world peace. But she had no idea how to go about doing so in practical terms. This was all the more reason why she was struck by the words *kosen-rufu in France*.

After the meeting, Murano approached the leader who had spoken and asked for an introduction to Mizusawa. A few days later, the three women met together. Mizusawa was about ten years Murano's senior.

"I would also like to devote my life to working for kosen-rufu in France," Murano began. "Is there any way you could take me with you?"

Taken aback by this sudden and unexpected request, Mizusawa asked: "Do you know anyone over there?"

"No," Murano replied.

"Do you speak French?"

"Not a word, but I will start studying now."

"Then why do you want to go to France?"

"Because I heard about your experience."

Whether the destination was America or Africa, Murano would no doubt have asked the same of anyone she met.

"I realize this may be quite an imposition," Murano added, "but please take me to France with you."

It was an audacious request, utterly lacking in forethought.

A S SHE LISTENED to Murano, the young women's leader who had set up the meeting began to panic, thinking: "It's because I said that the time has come for us to go out into the world that she has made this decision. I must tell her to consider things more carefully and calmly."

Having kindled Murano's enthusiasm, the leader now had to temper her fervor.

"Ms. Murano, what is your reason for wanting to go to France?" she asked.

"As I mentioned earlier, it is to work for kosen-rufu there," Murano replied.

"But I'm afraid that's not enough," the leader continued. "Unless you have a clear idea of how you will make a living over there, and how you will contribute to society, you will only end up being a burden on everyone."

Murano was annoyed. She felt that the leader was con-
tradicting the encouragement she had given at the meeting. Nevertheless, the passion that had been set ablaze in
her heart could not be extinguished. Concluding that
she should discuss this matter with her parents, Murano
parted ways with Masayo Mizusawa.

When she returned home, she shared her thoughts
with her parents, but they voiced strong disapproval. "It's
absurd for a young girl to go to a foreign country where
she knows no one. I won't allow you to do such a dangerous thing!" her mother exclaimed.

Murano was the fifth of seven sisters, and all her siblings had nothing but scathing remarks for her plan:
"You're dreaming!" "You're just dazzled by the thought
of the splendor of Paris. You need to calm down!"

Murano was bitterly frustrated that not even her family, all of whom were practicing Nichiren Buddhism,
could understand her sincere desire to devote herself to
kosen-rufu in France. Vowing in her heart that she would
go no matter what, she chanted with tears streaming
down her face.

Shortly thereafter, President Yamamoto presented
guidelines to the high school division in an editorial in
the November 1965 issue of *The Daibyakurenge* study
journal, entitled "Young Phoenixes, Take Flight Into the
Future!"

One line in particular caught Murano's eye: "Now is
the time for us to advance worldwide kosen-rufu, dedicating our lives to the realization of global peace." This fueled the flames of Murano's determination even further.

A T THE START OF 1966, Murano met again with Mizusawa. It was their third encounter. Murano's desire to move to France had become even stronger than when they first met.

"My decision will not change," Murano insisted. "I promise I will do my best not to cause you any problems, so please take me with you."

Until now, Mizusawa had painted a fairly grim picture of the realities of living in France with the intent of dissuading Murano, but the teenager's single-minded enthusiasm was beginning to have an effect on her. She thought to herself, *Someone like her might be a great asset to our movement in France.*

People are touched by earnestness and passion.

Mizusawa said to Murano, whose head was bowed in a gesture of entreaty: "I understand. You have my support. Let's go to France together."

Murano's eyes lit up. "Really? Thank you very much!"

"Well, then. You'd better start studying French right away," Mizusawa remarked. "Also, if you are unable to explain Buddhism to others in a convincing manner, you won't be able to contribute to kosen-rufu, so it's important that you introduce as many people as possible to the practice before we go. We'll probably leave toward the end of the year, so I'd like to see you help at least ten people take up faith by then."

Sharing her personal thoughts, Mizusawa then commented: "This will be my third trip to France. The last two were for the purpose of furthering my own education, but this time, it's different. I'm going there with a commitment to live the rest of my life working for kosen-rufu in that country. So let's do our best together."

Mizusawa first went to France in 1963. She was starting to gain recognition in Japan as an up-and-coming
young hairstylist, and made the trip in order to study the
latest styling techniques. Though she learned to speak
French through language classes, there were few salons in
France back then that would take on a Japanese trainee.
The whole point of her journey to France would have
been wasted if she could not pursue her studies. It was
around this time that Mizusawa was introduced to
Nichiren Buddhism by a Japanese woman with whom
she had become acquainted in France. Motivated by the
promise that all of her prayers would be answered without fail, she decided to give the practice a try.

SOON AFTER Mizusawa embraced faith, she started
seeing conspicuous results. Through the introduction of a person she had met by chance, she obtained an
internship at a leading hair salon in Paris. This was the
first benefit she received from her practice.

The following year, having greatly developed her skills
through her work experience, she returned to Japan for
a short stay. Her family ran a beauty salon and her mother
and two younger sisters were hairstylists. Mizusawa told
them about Buddhism, and they all joined the Soka
Gakkai.

She went back to Paris to continue her training, this
time accompanied by her youngest sister. During this
stay, she also immersed herself in Soka Gakkai activities
and, as a result, developed immensely both in faith and
her chosen field. Through the warm bonds she formed

with the local members, she began to feel a strong attachment to France.

Eight months later, however, she decided to return to Japan and work there with her newly acquired skills. She planned her trip so that she could fly back with French members who were going to attend the 1965 Soka Gakkai summer training course at the head temple, and participated as well. To her great surprise, during the training course, she was appointed as a leader of the young women's division in France.

Mizusawa thought to herself: *The fact that I have received this appointment must mean that I have a mission to work for kosen-rufu in France. The arena of my activities isn't limited to Japan!*

She thus determined to return to Paris as soon as possible. It would be her third trip there. However, her parents had been hoping that, with the training she had received in France, she could take over the family business. But after earnest discussion about the matter, it was decided that Masayo would make the move, on the condition that she would not rely on her parents for financial support. It was shortly after this that Murano approached her and asked if she could go to France as well.

For her part, Murano spent the next year studying French through a course offered on the radio. At the same time, she exerted herself energetically in sharing Nichiren Buddhism with her friends, enabling one person after another to start practicing.

Murano's father, who had been closely observing her actions, realized that his daughter was absolutely serious.

One day, he said to his wife: "We have seven daughters. Since President Yamamoto asserts that the time for worldwide kosen-rufu has come, perhaps we can allow at least one of them to go overseas."

And so Murano received permission to go to France.

MIZUSAWA AND MURANO'S trip to France was finally scheduled for the autumn of 1966. When the national young women's leaders learned of their plans, they arranged for the two women to participate in the summer training course at the head temple in August. There, they met with President Yamamoto, who was waiting for them under a tent set up on the temple grounds.

"We are going to France to work for kosen-rufu in Europe!" they reported.

"That's wonderful," Shin'ichi said. "I will be traveling there shortly to support your efforts, so let's meet again at that time."

Shin'ichi's words gave the young women courage.

Afterwards, Shin'ichi entrusted Young Women's Leader Yumie Fujiya with a parting gift of some money for Mizusawa and Murano, and asked her to organize a gathering to send them off. With Shin'ichi's gift, each of the young women bought a small altar in which to enshrine their Gohonzon in France. It was a purchase that reflected their deep commitment to carry out their practice in their new country.

At the end of September, they left for Paris. They first boarded a ship from the port of Yokohama and then made their way across the Eurasian continent by train and plane. It was October 2 when they reached Orly Airport outside of Paris.

As Murano stepped off the plane and onto French soil for the first time, her body trembled with emotion: *I finally made it. I'm going to dedicate my whole life to kosen-rufu here. I don't care if I never go back to Japan!*

She knew no one, had very little money and hardly spoke the language. But in her heart blazed a pure passion to realize kosen-rufu in France. Mizusawa felt the same way.

The day after they arrived, they went to visit the Kawasakis, who were still hospitalized in Orleans following their car accident. The husband and wife were lying in adjacent beds in the same room, their legs in casts.

When the two young women introduced themselves, Eiji Kawasaki said: "Let's work hard together. And with splendid proof of our development, let's go to Japan together to report to President Yamamoto."

Having just arrived in Paris and being firmly resolved to spend the rest of their lives there, Mizusawa and Murano were speechless at this proposition of going to Japan. The fact was, however, that reporting to President Yamamoto in Japan was a common goal of all the members in France.

WHEN THEY ARRIVED in Paris, Mizusawa and Murano stayed in an inexpensive hotel while they searched for jobs and an apartment. Eventually, Mizusawa started working as a hairstylist, serving a clientele of mostly wives of Japanese businessmen stationed in France. Murano worked as her assistant and also studied French at a language school.

Both women joyfully engaged in Soka Gakkai activities. Murano wanted to talk about Buddhism with every person she encountered. But since she did not have the language ability yet, she wrote down in French on a piece of paper: "Are you interested in Buddhism? Would you like to attend a meeting?" and showed it to whoever would read it.

Not being able to communicate verbally, all Murano could do was escort those who expressed an interest to the meeting. There, Eiji Kawasaki, who had been released from the hospital, or Shotaro Hasebe would kindly explain the practice to them. Through such efforts, Murano could help a handful of people take faith in the six or so months before Shin'ichi Yamamoto's trip to France in May 1967.

Now, at the Paris Community Center, Shin'ichi turned his gaze to Murano and Mizusawa, who stood behind her. It had been nine months since he had met with them at the Soka Gakkai summer training course in Japan, and he felt reassured seeing their beaming faces.

Another Japanese young woman was standing nearby, her resolute eyes fixed on Shin'ichi. Her name was Machiko Irise and she was an art student. After attending a fine arts university in Japan, she had moved to France to study commercial design. It was there that she heard about Buddhism and joined the Soka Gakkai.

Irise learned the basics of the practice from Françoise Walton-Violet, an art gallery manager who had been introduced to Buddhism by Hasebe three years earlier. Having witnessed her daughter's recovery from asthma as a result of her chanting, Walton-Violet had gained great conviction in the practice. As she strove to study

64 • THE NEW HUMAN REVOLUTION

and share Buddhism with others, she gradually awakened to her mission for kosen-rufu. Thus, the first native French leader was born.

Walton-Violet was a person of great self-discipline and tenacity. She chanted abundantly and never compromised when it came to achieving a goal in Soka Gakkai activities. It was she who gave her all to explaining Buddhism and the Soka Gakkai spirit to Irise, helping the latter to develop in faith.

ON SUNDAY mornings, Françoise Walton-Violet called Machiko Irise to wake her up so that they could recite the sutra and chant Nam-myoho-renge-kyo together. And when there were no guests at a discussion meeting, she would say to the other members present: "Let's go out right now and talk to our friends. The purpose of discussion meetings is to share Buddhism. There's not much point being here if it's only us, is there?" She would then organize everyone to do just that.

When German Nazi forces invaded France during World War II, Walton-Violet and her husband joined the Resistance movement. Her husband was later arrested by the Nazi secret police and killed. This was all the more reason why she longed for peace from the depths of her life. She keenly felt that peace was not something bestowed from without, but something that had to be won by defeating the negative tendencies inherent in people and in power. This made her approach all matters with the utmost seriousness. And it was why she would not tolerate a casual, halfhearted or irresponsible attitude toward Buddhist activities.

Inspired by Walton-Violet's endeavors, Machiko Irise deepened her faith and her commitment to sharing the practice with others.

The ability to nurture and raise people is not determined by the length of our practice. Just as a single burning piece of firewood serves to kindle other logs, our ardent passion to realize kosen-rufu touches the hearts of our fellow members and helps them grow.

In this way, driven by the spirit of the young women's members from Japan, the Soka Gakkai organization in France initiated a hope-filled advance.

Shin'ichi said to them: "Each of you is a Joan of Arc of the Mystic Law dedicating your youth to working for kosen-rufu in France. You have a wondrous mission. I hope that, together with me, you will walk the great path of kosen-rufu throughout your life!"

The young women never forgot the pledge they made to Shin'ichi. Later, they would all become central figures of the French organization, with Sadae Murano serving as the national women's leader.

SHIN'ICHI YAMAMOTO smiled warmly as he approached the four members who had traveled from the United Kingdom to attend the Gohonzon-enshrinement ceremony at the Paris Community Center.

Addressing Eiko Rich, who had just been appointed the leader of London Chapter that day, he said: "The time has come for our UK organization to make a fresh departure. It is important to have the determination to continuously advance with renewed vigor.

"Nichiren Daishonin writes: 'Be diligent in developing your faith until the last moment of your life. Otherwise you will have regrets' (WND, 1027). As human beings, it is our tendency to give in to inertia, no matter how strong our determination initially may be. When this happens, though we may appear to be making great efforts, in actuality, we lose our momentum and end up getting nowhere. What enables us to break out of this stalemate is the spirit of challenge, the spirit that everything begins from now, from today. I hope that you will always maintain vibrant faith that ever brims with fresh hope."

Shin'ichi next took commemorative photographs with the members who had come from West Germany and the other countries that comprised Europe No. 2 Headquarters. Of the fifty or so people present, about half were women of Japanese descent. Among them, Shin'ichi recognized the familiar faces of Yukiko Sada, the wife of headquarters leader Koichiro Sada, and

Michiyo Moro'oka, the wife of vice headquarters leader Michiya Moro'oka. Matsuko Takaishi, a doctor who was responsible for the young women's division in Europe, was also present.

Shin'ichi once again came across several new young women's members. Having moved to West Germany from Japan within the past year, most of them were working in hospitals as nurses and in other positions. They, too, had gone to their new home country determined to dedicate their lives to worldwide kosen-rufu.

In response to an appeal made by Koichiro Sada and others, ten young men had moved to West Germany from Japan two years earlier to work in coal mines. Now, at the encouragement of Matsuko Takaishi, a growing number of young women's members were also settling there.

Shin'ichi had met four of these women shortly before their departure from Japan and said to them: "Nichiren Daishonin reminds us 'not to expect good times, but take the bad times for granted' (WND, 998). Please go to West Germany with the attitude that it is only natural to face hardships. The point is to never be defeated. I hope that you will not be swayed by your emotions or become discouraged. Winning over our weaknesses is the same as winning in life."

THE FIRST CHALLENGE the young women's members from Japan took on when they arrived in West Germany was learning the language. Working in hospitals as they did, not communicating well could result in serious accidents. They therefore put great effort into their studies.

One of these young women, Yoriko Takei, started out by asking her Japanese friends who could already speak the language to translate and write down for her what she wanted to say in German. She then memorized the phrases in order to communicate with doctors and patients. After her shift each day, she went to a language school and studied.

About three months after her arrival, however, she was assigned to the late shift at the hospital and could no longer attend her language classes. Still far from fluent, she was severely reprimanded time and again by doctors who told her: "Your pronunciation is terrible! I can't understand a word you're saying!" Some of the other nurses even snickered when she was admonished in this way.

But no matter how much she wanted to study German in earnest, her circumstances simply didn't permit her to do so. Whenever a doctor yelled at her, she would feel worthless, fighting back tears with all her might. At such times, she would recall President Yamamoto's encouragement never to be defeated, no matter what, and think: *If I lose heart now, it will spell my defeat! I'll show everyone that I can master the language, even if I can't go to classes!*

When faced with difficulties, the question is: will we hesitate and stop in our tracks, or will we muster up courage and charge ahead? Herein lies the key to our victory or defeat.

Takei began to study German by herself as if her life depended on it. She carried her dictionary with her at all times and studied wherever she could, including during her commute to work and in bed before going to sleep at night.

The young women from Japan also engaged enthusiastically in Soka Gakkai activities. They shared Buddhism with everyone they knew, including their co-workers.

One example was Eriko Chino, who worked as a clinical lab technician at a hospital in Duisburg in the western part of the country. She would often spend an hour or two traveling on trains or buses in order to meet with members to encourage them in faith or to talk to friends about Nichiren Buddhism. Through her efforts, six young women began to practice in Essen, near Duisburg. In her propagation efforts, Chino even went to neighboring countries, including the Netherlands, Denmark and Sweden.

Determined that their endeavors were going to change history, these young women pledged to each other to continuously take action for kosen-rufu.

SHIN'ICHI YAMAMOTO addressed the young women who had traveled to France from West Germany for the enshrinement ceremony, saying: "I see that the young women's division, which represents a flower garden of kosen-rufu, is developing wonderfully in West Germany as well.

"Blossoms herald the arrival of spring, inspiring hope and joy in all. In addition, their growth influences everything around them. It could be said that the young women's division is of utmost importance to the eternal advancement of the kosen-rufu movement. When the young women develop, the Soka Gakkai develops.

"Eventually, the members of the young women's division will graduate into the women's division, the core of our organization. They will shoulder the responsibility of raising children—the successors of kosen-rufu—and will be a beacon for their families and relatives. In other words, the degree to which the young women's members grow and develop their abilities now will determine the future course of our movement. Meeting all of you today gives me great confidence that the future of West Germany and the rest of Europe is secure."

After taking commemorative photos with everyone, Shin'ichi, who had been speaking to the members nonstop, felt dizzy, perhaps because of exhaustion.

The white flowers of the horse-chestnut trees dotting the city swayed gently in the breeze. Their pristine beauty brought to Shin'ichi's mind an image of the smiling faces of the young women's division members.

On May 23, Shin'ichi and his party traveled to Rome, Italy. He had a full itinerary that day showing High Priest Nittatsu and the others around the city, but also wanted to meet and encourage an art student from Japan who was living there. The student's name was Yasuo Kojima, and he was the younger brother of Sumiko Kojima, who was also studying painting there.

The couple who had been serving as the district leaders in Rome, Masao and Kimie Yamagishi, had returned to Japan for Masao's job the previous year, and Shin'ichi was now looking to raise new leaders in their stead.

His opportunity to speak to Yasuo Kojima presented itself in the elevator of the hotel where he was staying. Seeing Yasuo's thin frame, Shin'ichi began their exchange expressing concern for the young man's health.

Moved by Shin'ichi's kind words, Yasuo felt the flame of determination kindle in his heart. Shin'ichi appointed him the young men's district leader of Rome, and presented him with a medal. Engraved with the image of an eagle, the medal had been created to commemorate the seventh anniversary of Shin'ichi's inauguration as president of the Soka Gakkai.

No matter how busy our schedules may be, if we are firmly resolved to meet with others, we can always find the time. Moreover, even if the encounter is brief, our earnest words, imbued with wholehearted prayer and sincerity, will deeply touch the other person's life.

ON THE AFTERNOON of May 25, Shin'ichi and his party flew to Zurich, Switzerland. He encouraged the three young men who met them at the airport, one of whom was Kojiro Takayama.

Shin'ichi was well acquainted with the youth's mother, Sachi. She was one of the members who had welcomed him on his first visit there. Since that time, she had married a Swiss man and changed her name to Sachi Bruno. As the central figure of the organization in Switzerland, she was actively promoting Soka Gakkai activities.

Shaking Kojiro's hand, Shin'ichi thanked him and said: "Please do your best for the sake of the happiness of the Swiss people."

"I will!" Kojiro replied energetically.

Kojiro had just moved there from Japan three months earlier. Shin'ichi sensed in his determined tone that Sachi's strong resolve to teach her son about faith was having a positive effect.

Kojiro was born in Fukushima Prefecture in February

1944. His father was killed in action during World War II. Following the war, Sachi and her son went to live with relatives in Kuroiso, in neighboring Tochigi Prefecture. Shortly thereafter, however, Sachi found a job as a live-in housekeeper in Hayama, Kanagawa Prefecture, and had to entrust the care of Kojiro to a relative. It pained her deeply to have to live away from her son, who was still quite young.

Whenever she was out shopping or doing something else and saw children who were about the same age as her son, her thoughts would turn to Kojiro and her heart would ache. Night after night, she would clutch her pillow and weep, thinking of him.

It was in Hayama that Sachi was introduced to Nichiren Buddhism. With the hope that it would help her son become happy, she decided to give the practice a try. When Kojiro subsequently came for a visit, she asked some youth members to meet with him and tell him about faith.

Later, her employer announced that he was going to be transferred to Switzerland for work and asked Sachi to accompany him and his family there. His request bespoke the high esteem in which he held Sachi's character and abilities.

By then, Kojiro was already in high school. Thinking of her son, Sachi had hesitated to accept the proposal, but in the end could not pass up the opportunity. She therefore moved to Switzerland, and it was there that she began to consider the possibility of remarrying.

IN HER NEW COUNTRY, Sachi met a Swiss man who fell in love with her. His name was Albert Bruno, and he was a repair technician for an electric company. Finding him to be sincere and gentle, Sachi came to reciprocate his feelings. Before long, they began to discuss marriage. But the son she had left behind in Japan was now seventeen years old, a particularly turbulent and emotional age. Imagining the shock that her marriage plans might cause him, she could not bring herself to take the plunge.

In October 1961, when Sachi met Shin'ichi Yamamoto at Geneva Airport on his first visit to Europe, she was in the middle of this dilemma. She therefore told him her situation and asked him for guidance. Shin'ichi encouraged her to speak frankly with her son.

She then wrote a letter to her son Kojiro, soliciting his thoughts on her plans to marry. His response was: "I wholeheartedly support you." He actually did have some mixed feelings, but he did not want to say anything that might cast a shadow over his mother's happiness. Six months later, Sachi received another letter from Kojiro announcing that he had joined the Soka Gakkai.

In March of that year, Kojiro graduated from high school and started working for a trading company in Tokyo. But having grown up in the unspoiled environment of rural Kuroiso, he could not bear life in the big city, which he found almost suffocating. In particular, he had difficulties in his relationships with other people.

It was then that he heard about the Soka Gakkai once again from a friend of his who was a student. Kojiro was rather skeptical of religion and had resisted at first.

However, moved by the attitude of his friend, who listened intently to his problems and was sincere in his interactions, he began to practice.

As she read of her son's decision to join the Soka Gakkai, Sachi wept tears of joy. She had continuously chanted Nam-myoho-renge-kyo for her son to take faith and become happy. Shortly after receiving his letter, she and Bruno married.

While Kojiro had become a Soka Gakkai member, he was not yet active in the organization. When she learned of this, Sachi began to chant with even greater intensity, praying that he would stand up in his practice so that he could transform his karma and savor genuine happiness.

There is nothing more powerful than the determination of a mother when it comes to the well-being of her child.

A COUPLE OF YEARS LATER, Bruno said to Sachi: "What do you think about asking your son to come and live together with us in Switzerland?"

While Sachi deeply appreciated her husband's thoughtful consideration, she also had some reservations. She was worried about how well Kojiro would fare in a country where the language and culture were so different. She decided to write to him anyway and ask him what he thought. In the letter, she mentioned her husband's proposal and then expressed her own concerns that if he were to join them, he might have difficulty learning the language and consequently face many hardships.

But Kojiro replied that he was eager to come to

Switzerland. It had been his dream since childhood to live with his mother.

After all the necessary arrangements for his move were finally completed, Kojiro joined his mother, stepfather and new half-sister in Switzerland in February 1967. They thus began their life as a family of four.

Never having had a father figure, Kojiro didn't know how to interact with his stepfather. The language barrier also put him under heavy stress, making heartfelt communication between the two men nearly impossible. He enrolled in a school to learn French, but that too proved to be a major challenge. Before long, anxiety and worry about his future began to set in as well.

Over time, Kojiro became more and more withdrawn and introverted. Tormented by an acute sense of loneliness and psychologically drained, he eventually found himself on the verge of a nervous breakdown. Sometimes, he would confide in Sachi that he thought everyone around him was making fun of him.

Seeing her child suffering such mental anguish was unbearable for Sachi. She devoted every spare moment she could find to chanting for her son. As she chanted Nam-myoho-renge-kyo, she thought: *This is an opportunity for Kojiro to start practicing in earnest. It's a turning point. The real struggle begins now. I will absolutely not be defeated!*

She also encouraged her son: "Now is the time for you to stand up in your practice. You have to win with faith!"

MOVED BY his mother's appeal, Kojiro began to sincerely apply himself to his practice. He even accompanied her when she would go and encourage members. His countenance grew brighter each day as his anxiety dissipated, and he started to see a glimmer of hope. Little by little, he warmed up to his stepfather and could have a conversation with him. Kojiro had indeed begun to experience the power of practicing Buddhism.

Now, on this day, May 25, 1967, Kojiro had traveled from Geneva to Zurich to welcome Shin'ichi Yamamoto and his party. He and the other young men who had come to the airport carried the visitors' luggage to the hotel.

Keenly sensing the great victory of Sachi's prayers for her son, Shin'ichi thanked Kojiro for his help and asked him to convey his very best regards to his mother.

The single-minded prayer of a mother to see her child become happy and to teach him or her about faith always bears fruit. The key is to firmly resolve that you are going to see your prayers realized no matter what and then chant abundantly, never giving up.

Children deepen their understanding and appreciation of the practice by observing their parents' attitude and way of life. It is therefore crucial that parents continue to polish themselves, developing the strength and character to overcome all obstacles and exhibiting warm consideration toward others. This is how we demonstrate the greatness of Buddhist practice.

Ultimately, the onus rests with parents, as Buddhists, to transmit faith to their children. Therein lies an act of genuine love.

On May 27, the stage of Shin'ichi's activities moved from Switzerland, the land of the Alps, to Amsterdam, the Netherlands, his final destination on this guidance tour.

A handful of members were waiting at the airport in Amsterdam for President Yamamoto to arrive—a Japanese youth named Seizo Onodera, two young couples and two small children. Almost an hour had passed since the airplane carrying Shin'ichi and his party had landed. All the other passengers on the flight had disembarked, but there was still no sign of Shin'ichi.

"I wonder what could have happened to President Yamamoto," murmured a concerned-looking woman of Japanese descent among the group. Her name was Ichiko Price, and she was the leader of Holland District.

WHEN SEIZO ONODERA went to an airline employee to inquire after Shin'ichi and his party, he was told that they had left some time earlier. Realizing they had missed them, the members decided to make their way over to Shin'ichi's hotel.

The family of Aiko Simon, the district women's leader, opted for going home because one of their children had become carsick on the way to the airport and was not feeling well. Onodera and the Prices thus went to the hotel themselves, but when they arrived there, they were told that Shin'ichi had stepped out. They waited in the lobby until he returned.

"Sensei," Onodera called out when he spotted Shin'ichi. After identifying himself, he remarked: "We waited for you at the airport, but as we didn't find you there, we came to the hotel."

"You were at the airport?" Shin'ichi said apologetically. "I'm terribly sorry for the inconvenience. Come, let's meet in my room."

There, a conversation ensued, but the local members remained stiff and formal. It was only when Shin'ichi's wife, Mineko, served some cold juice that they began to relax.

Shin'ichi had seen Onodera at the enshrinement ceremony at the Paris Community Center, but he thought he looked much more worn out than he had just a week earlier. Shin'ichi was always concerned about the welfare of his fellow members.

"Has something happened?" Shin'ichi asked.

"I quit my job at the hotel," Onodera blurted out.

The twenty-eight-year-old youth had been practicing for six years. He had been working at a hotel in Japan until eight months earlier, when he was transferred as a trainee to an affiliated hotel in Rotterdam in the southwest of the country.

Onodera related to Shin'ichi the events that led to his resignation. He had asked a colleague to switch shifts with him so that he could attend the enshrinement ceremony in Paris on the 20th. He planned to catch a train immediately after the ceremony and return to Rotterdam the same day, but he missed his train. When he called the hotel and explained the situation to his colleague who was working his shift, the colleague said he would cover for him.

D
URING THE TULIP SEASON in May, the hotels in Holland are overflowing with tourists and busier than at any other time of year.

Feeling terrible about missing his shift, Seizo Onodera caught the train back to Rotterdam the day after the enshrinement ceremony in Paris. When he arrived at the hotel, the general manager was standing in the lobby waiting for him, his arms crossed. "You are a trainee!" the manager yelled. "What on earth were you thinking? If you are going to be so irresponsible, you should go back to Japan!"

There was nothing Onodera could say to defend himself. At first, he bowed his head and apologized repeatedly, but when the manager showed no sign of letting up his tirade, Onodera lost his temper.

"I get it!" Onodera retorted. "If that's the case, then I quit!"

To receive training in a hotel in Europe was considered a great privilege for Japanese trying to work in the hotel business, and it was a huge asset to one's future career in Japan. But with his actions, Onodera had thrown that opportunity away.

As he finished relaying this chain of events to Shin'-ichi Yamamoto, he said despondently: "My behavior was rash and impulsive."

Sensing that the young man deeply regretted his actions and that he had been suffering tremendously ever since, Shin'ichi smiled gently and remarked: "I see. What an awful experience that must have been for you."

This is not what Onodera expected to hear. He thought that Shin'ichi would point out where he went wrong and give him strict guidance. Touched by Shin'-ichi's warmth, tears of relief welled up in his eyes.

"Mr. Onodera, it won't do any good to have regrets about the past," Shin'ichi added. "We need to live for tomorrow, for the future. You're still young. To be young is to have limitless potential. And the way we tap that potential is by not devaluing or doubting ourselves over one mistake or failure.

"I hope you will continue to press forward, never fearing failure. Everything is decided from now. Win tomorrow! Don't be defeated!"

"I'll do my best!" Onodera replied.

"So what are your plans now? Are you OK financially?" Shin'ichi inquired

ONODERA DIDN'T KNOW how to respond to Shin'ichi's question regarding his future plans. He had been pondering this question himself over the past few days, but had not reached any conclusion. He therefore asked himself once again: *What was my original purpose in coming to Europe? The most obvious reason was to receive training in hotel management, but ultimately wasn't it in order to contribute to worldwide kosen-rufu?*

Onodera thought quietly for a moment, and then declared to Shin'ichi: "I've got some money set aside, so I should be able to support myself for the time being. I will stay here. I will take whatever job I can get, so that I can dedicate my life to kosen-rufu in the Netherlands."

No sooner had he said this than Shin'ichi cried: "That's right! That's the spirit! All honest work is respectworthy. You came to this country because you have a mission here. It's important that you do your best and persevere until the very end.

"Life's struggle is determined by how we pick ourselves up once we've hit bottom. That is the point from which our flight toward true victory begins. You have my total support."

Their conversation continued in a friendly manner. For Shin'ichi, however, it was an intense effort to offer guidance that would penetrate the young man's life.

As the meeting was winding down, Shin'ichi said to everyone present: "Let's recite the sutra and chant Nam-myoho-renge-kyo together and pray for the health and happiness of the members as well as for the development of our organization here."

They commenced with their prayers in Shin'ichi's hotel room. Shin'ichi prayed wholeheartedly for Nichiren Buddhism to spread throughout the Netherlands, the country's prosperity and the growth of all the members there.

After finishing the prayers, Shin'ichi asked Eiji Kawasaki: "As I recall, a district has already been established here. Is that correct?"

"Yes," Kawasaki replied. "Ichiko Price is the district leader, and Aiko Simon is the women's leader. Currently, they have a handful of members."

"I would like to form a chapter here—what do you think? It may be the smallest Soka Gakkai chapter in the world to date, but I'd like to make a cause now for great advancement in the future."

The members nodded and smiled in a show of their approval for Shin'ichi's proposal.

AFTER CONFIRMING that everyone was in agreement, Shin'ichi said: "Then it's settled, we'll establish a chapter. Staying with the leadership appointments already in place, I'd like to name Ichiko Price the chapter leader, and Aiko Simon, who's not here today, the chapter women's leader. I would also like Mr. On-odera to take on the big responsibility of young men's general chapter leader."

"I'll do my best!" Onodera replied, looking somewhat nervous.

Shin'ichi then addressed the husband of Ichiko Price, who was Dutch and also a member, and asked if he would become the chapter young men's leader. When Onodera finished translating for him, Price replied in the affirmative in Japanese.

"A new chapter has just been formed. Today marks a fresh departure for the Netherlands!" Shin'ichi announced.

It was a brief encounter, but it constituted a historical moment. Through the heart-to-heart exchanges that took place that day, the torch of kosen-rufu in Holland was lit.

Shin'ichi presented the new leaders with cloths for wrapping prayer beads and other gifts to celebrate their appointments. Concerned about Onodera's situation, he also gave the young man some canned food and other provisions that he and his party had brought from Japan. It was more than Onodera could carry.

"Mr. Onodera, no matter how difficult the circumstances you find yourself in, I hope you will never lose confidence in yourself," Shin'ichi said. "The worst thing is to be defeated by your own weaknesses. You may not find a job right away, but I want you to continue pressing forward. Of utmost importance is that you keep challenging your situation with hope and courage, until the very end. This is the Soka Gakkai spirit."

Finally, Shin'ichi suggested that the two of them meet again the following day.

From the hotel, Onodera headed directly to the home of Mr. and Mrs. Simon to report to them about the meeting. Through Shin'ichi's encouragement, his dejection had transformed into determination, his anxiety into joy. There was a bounce in his step as he walked.

Upon hearing the news of the formation of Holland Chapter, Aiko Simon exclaimed: "That's wonderful, but at the same time I feel really bad that we've been made a chapter with so few members."

"That's why we have to make greater efforts to spread Nichiren Buddhism," Onodera replied. "Our struggle begins today."

O N THE MORNING of May 28, the following day, Simon accompanied Onodera to Shin'ichi Yamamoto's hotel. Shin'ichi was scheduled to fly back to Japan that afternoon, but he invited them up to his room and spoke with them until it was time to go.

Addressing Simon, Shin'ichi said: "Mrs. Simon, thank you for coming today. With the formation of Holland Chapter, I would like to ask you to take on the responsibility of chapter women's leader. What do you think?"

"I hardly feel qualified, but I will do my best," Simon replied.

"That's wonderful. By the way, where is your husband today?" Shin'ichi inquired.

"He is home looking after our children."

"I'm sorry that I won't be able to meet him. The truth is, I was thinking of appointing him as district leader."

"I see. I'm certain he would accept."

"Please convey to him my hope that he will give it his all."

Onodera then spoke up, his voice full of resolve. "Sensei, we are determined to increase our membership in the Netherlands and to realize great development."

Simon nodded in agreement.

Smiling, Shin'ichi said: "Rather than thinking of expanding the organization right away, it's better to first establish a solid core. Even if you are small in number, if you build an organization that is united through strong bonds of friendship and brimming with the joy of faith, waves of kosen-rufu will naturally ripple outward.

"In addition, in order to achieve tremendous growth in the future, it's important that each person put their utmost effort into confronting and winning in every challenge that arises on the path of kosen-rufu. It is the accumulation of small victories that ultimately leads to momentous victory.

"The struggle for kosen-rufu is about perseverance. There may be times when, having overcome one obstacle after another, we are a hairsbreadth away from reaching our objective. If, however, at that point, we let our guard down and become lazy, everything will come to naught. As Nichiren Daishonin states: 'Be diligent in developing your faith until the last moment of your life. Otherwise you will have regrets' (WND, 1027). Therefore, we must never relax our efforts or give up. Rather, we need to cause the flame of our passion and fighting spirit to burn ever brighter, winning over our struggles every step of the way, until the very last moment of our lives."

Shin'ichi then recited the sutra and chanted Nam-myoho-renge-kyo together with his guests.

W HEN THEY FINISHED chanting, it was time for Shin'ichi and the other leaders from Japan to leave for the airport. In the hotel lobby, Shin'ichi said to Onodera in parting: "Holland is a beautiful place. The flowers, the windmills, the canals—it's like a fairy-tale setting. I hope you will strive with all your might and paint the masterpiece of your life here.

"As long as you persevere in your practice, you will absolutely achieve total victory, becoming the great hero of your life's drama. Let's win! Let's definitely win! I'll be waiting for news of your victories. Let's meet again. When we do, I'm sure you'll be standing tall, proud and triumphant."

Shin'ichi's encouragement over these two days transformed Onodera's life. Strengthening his resolve to devote his life to kosen-rufu in Holland, the young man moved from Rotterdam to the capital, Amsterdam, where it would be easier to carry out Soka Gakkai activities. There he found a job working as an interpreter and guide for tourists.

After moving on to employment with an airline company and then overseeing passenger service for a transport company, he became the owner of a hotel. Coming twenty-one years after his encounter with Shin'ichi, this was undeniable proof of his magnificent victory.

Onodera would continue exerting himself wholeheartedly in Soka Gakkai activities, eventually as the general director of the Netherlands.

Life's true victory is found in our efforts to live out our lives dedicated to kosen-rufu.

The airplane carrying Shin'ichi and his party departed from the airport in Amsterdam at 1:40 PM on May 28. From the window, they could see below them rows of medieval-style buildings and the numerous canals criss-crossing the city. The fresh spring foliage lining the canals sparkled brilliantly in the sunlight.

New leaves are a symbol of hope, their hue the color of youth.

For Shin'ichi, this image exemplified the valiant, young Bodhisattvas of the Earth who were emerging across the globe, awakened to their mission for kosen-rufu.

If youth stand up, a new day will dawn. If youth develop, the way forward will open.

As Shin'ichi turned his thoughts to the future of the youth, he felt the sun of hope rising in his heart and became invigorated. The exhaustion from his long trip seemed to vanish instantly.

NOTES

1. Seneca, *Dialogues and Letters,* edited and translated by C.D.N. Costa (London: Penguin Books, 1997), p. 20.

2. Seven Bells: The term given to the seven seven-year periods marking the history of the Soka Gakkai's development from its founding in 1930 through 1979. Shin'ichi introduced this concept (which second Soka Gakkai president Josei Toda had developed) on May 3, 1958, shortly after President Toda's death. He was then youth division chief of the general staff.

3. Oneness of body and mind: The Buddhist principle that the two seemingly distinct phenomena of body, or the physical aspect of life, and mind, or its spiritual aspect, are essentially non-dual, being two integral phases of a single reality.

Community
Spirit

THE CONSTANT POUNDING of waves eventually wears away rocks lining the seashore. We must continuously make fresh departures, advance and initiate new struggles! For herein lies the path to great victory in life and the movement to realize kosen-rufu.

On May 29, 1967, Shin'ichi Yamamoto returned to Japan from his trip to the United States and Europe. Hardly taking a moment to rest, he quickly set out to encourage members living in Osaka, in Hikone City in neighboring Shiga Prefecture, as well as in other parts of Japan. On June 23, he traveled to Matsushiro in Nagano Prefecture.[1]

For the past two years, Matsushiro had been experiencing a series of earthquakes, and the residents there were living in uncertainty and fear. Shin'ichi had wanted to go to Matsushiro for some time to meet with the members, but until now he couldn't find time in his extremely demanding schedule. In tandem with his visit, a commemorative photo session with group leaders of Nagano Joint Headquarters was planned for the following day, June 24, in Matsumoto, a major city in the prefecture.

Matsushiro lies in the southeast of Nagano City and is adjacent to the Chikuma River. Flourishing as a castle town during the Edo period,[2] it was the birthplace of Sakuma Shozan, a well-known scholar and intellectual from that era. It is also located near the site of the famous Battle of Kawanakajima, a battle fought between the two warlords Uesugi Kenshin and Takeda Shingen in the sixteenth century. Later, toward the end of World War II, a top-secret plan to move Japan's Imperial Headquarters to Matsushiro was set in motion and a giant underground military facility that covered an area of more than seven miles was constructed below three mountains in the region.

The recent series of earthquakes afflicting Matsushiro had begun on August 3, 1965. On that day, amid the blazing heat of summer, the residents heard intermittent explosive booms in the distance. Assuming that they were dynamite explosions set off by construction crews building mountain passes, at first no one paid any particular attention to them. But in fact, the blast sounds and three unfelt tremors that were recorded that day marked the beginning of continual earthquakes that would plague the people of Matsushiro for years to come.

The focus of the earthquakes was detected within a three-mile radius around Mount Minakami to the east of Matsushiro. It was noted by the Matsushiro Seismological Observatory, which had been set up after World War II at the planned site of the Imperial Headquarters.

O N AUGUST 1, 1965, two new pieces of equipment began operating at the Matsushiro Observatory. One was a strainmeter for measuring expansion and contraction of the earth, the other a seismometer installed as part of the Worldwide Standardized Seismic Network. The local observatory was one of the 125 stations of this network, which was being established across the globe at the time. The Matsushiro earthquakes started two days later.

By mid-August, a fluorescent glow known as the luminous phenomenon caused by earthquakes could be detected in the night sky. On August 20, the observatory reported to the Japan Meteorological Agency that an earthquake swarm—a group of frequent, relatively small tremors—was taking place in a specific area. By that day, some 2,288 tremors were recorded, only thirty-eight of which were perceptible. Of the perceptible quakes, thirty-seven had a registered intensity of one on the JMA Seismic Intensity Scale,[3] and were felt by many people inside buildings. One of them was a two, strong enough only to make a hanging lamp slightly swing. In general, most residents still hadn't noticed the tremors.

On August 24, the observatory reported the situation to the local municipal office. Before long, newspapers began carrying stories on the earthquakes, resulting in a heightened awareness among local residents.

On August 28, a Soka Gakkai Headquarters leaders meeting was held at the Taito Gymnasium in Tokyo, at which Kawanakajima Chapter was established as part of Nagano No. 2 Headquarters. The new chapter included Matsushiro. Filled with joy at this development, the chapter members began enthusiastically striving to build a tranquil and prosperous community through their Gakkai activities. They resolved to extend a network of friendship and trust among their neighbors and create a harmonious environment.

On September 2, updates about the earthquakes were broadcast to the residents of Matsushiro over the town's public address system, and on the 10th a pamphlet titled "Earthquake Information and Emergency Preparations" was distributed to each home in the area. Local school-teachers conducted earthquake drills for their students, instructing them in such safety procedures as placing cushions over their heads and kneeling under their desks to protect themselves in the event of a quake.

From September, the tremors grew more intense. In that month, there were 8,539 imperceptible quakes, 187 perceptible quakes with an intensity of level one, and eighteen with an intensity of two. Even the most opti-mistic residents were now becoming extremely anxious, fearing that all of this seismic activity must be the pre-lude to a major earthquake.

THE FIRST QUAKE with a seismic intensity of three was recorded at the Matsushiro Seismological Observatory on October 1. Houses shook and doors and windows rattled. There were 573 tremors in total that day, of which eighteen were perceptible. On October 6, the Nagano Regional Meteorological Observatory and the Matsushiro Observatory submitted data on the seismic activity they had been collecting since the beginning of August to the Japan Meteorological Agency. They also released the first official report on the situation.

The report stated that while there were changes in the degree of seismic activity, the focal point of the tremors hadn't moved, and so it was unlikely that the earthquake swarm would lead directly to a major quake or volcanic eruption. The local residents were relieved when they heard this news. But three days later, on October 9, the JMA announced a completely different interpretation of the same data. This stated that judging from past experience, the current increase in seismic activity was indicative of an earthquake capable of causing local damage.

The newspapers jumped on this unprecedented statement by the JMA and carried headlines blaring, "Earthquake Predicted!" and "Earthquake Alert!" Residents were thrown into confusion by this new information, which was completely contradictory to that released by the local agencies. The heads of the Nagano and Matsushiro observatories challenged the JMA's analysis and protested the agency's statements. The mayor of Matsushiro addressed the local citizenry through the town's public address system, calling on the people not to be deceived by uncorroborated information and declaring that he would contest the JMA's conclusions as their representative.

The question of whether to emphasize the possibility of safety or of danger represents a basic difference in thinking that was highlighted by these two divergent reports.

When there is a lack of coordination between organizations or institutions that the public relies on and inconsistent information is disseminated, it can cause anxiety and unnecessary confusion and undermine the solidarity needed for dealing with emergency situations. Awareness of the potential disaster that disunity and poor communication can lead to is crucial.

O N OCTOBER 11, the Matsushiro Earthquake Relief Headquarters was established with the town mayor as its leader. From about this time, the number and intensity of the tremors increased, and residents' anxiety mounted. They began to fear that a major earthquake might indeed be on its way.

The biggest tremors usually occurred between midnight and dawn. They would start with a low rumbling sound from below the earth. As the locals braced themselves for what was to come next, their homes began to shake. Everyone kept emergency packs filled with food rations and other supplies, as well as their valuables, near their beds. Many also slept in their street clothes so that they could evacuate at a moment's notice.

As the quakes grew in size and frequency, wild rumors and speculation spread rapidly. Some said they were a sign that Mount Minakami was going to erupt. Others insisted that the spirits of workers who died excavating the Imperial Headquarters military compound were causing them, while still others claimed they were the result of nuclear testing by the United States and the Soviet Union. Such spurious reports only fanned the locals' unease. Consequently, the mayor had to make an urgent plea asking residents to ignore everything except the official announcements from the Earthquake Relief Headquarters.

On November 4 and 5, earthquakes registering an intensity of four occurred. Houses shook violently, vases were overturned and objects toppled off shelves. Cracks appeared in the walls of older homes, and in some cases tiles fell from rooftops. On November 9, two Clean Government Party Upper House representatives arrived in Matsushiro to assess the situation.

The only way to fully grasp the facts of any given situation is to see the reality for oneself. Making decisions based on hearsay and assumptions is certain to lead to errors, and cannot result in effective countermeasures. Always personally going to the front lines is the iron rule of leaders who stand on the side of the people.

The Clean Government Party representatives met with the head of the prefectural Fire Fighting and Disaster Prevention Department, the mayor of Matsushiro and the heads of the Matsushiro Seismological Observatory and the Nagano Regional Meteorological Observatory, and were briefed on the situation facing the residents. They were also informed of the current status of the earthquakes, as well as forecasts of future seismic activity and what earthquake safety measures were in place. The Clean Government Party representatives were the first of any political party to visit the scene.

THE CLEAN GOVERNMENT representatives were shocked to discover through their inquiries that, while the local Matsushiro government had been seriously exploring various earthquake measures—such as stocking emergency food and water supplies—nothing was being done on the prefectural level, not even the establishment of an earthquake relief headquarters. They lost no time in visiting the prefectural government offices, where they met with the deputy governor and secured his promise that immediate action would be taken to create emergency relief procedures.

As soon as news about the Matsushiro earthquakes hit the newspapers, Shin'ichi Yamamoto contacted Nagano No. 2 Headquarters Leader Akira Kuroki and asked him to visit the members in Matsushiro and encourage them with all his might, and then to report back to him the details of their situation after each visit.

As the earthquakes intensified, Shin'ichi grew more concerned. Thinking of how anxiety must have been keeping the Matsushiro residents awake at night was causing him to lose sleep as well. He continued to chant for them.

On November 11, Kuroki was scheduled to go and visit the members in Matsushiro. Just before he left, he met with Shin'ichi at the Soka Gakkai Headquarters, who said to him: "Matsushiro is the place where, toward the end of World War II, the military government built a huge underground facility that was to house the Imperial Headquarters. It is said that many of the Korean people who were forcibly brought to Japan to supply the labor for the bunker died. The town has an incredibly tragic past. And now, twenty years later, the residents are being tormented by earthquakes.

"I believe that the time has come to change Matsushiro's history of suffering, for it to transform its destiny. Toward that end, the members there need to become a unifying force bringing all the people of Matsushiro together so that they can overcome the challenges presented by their current dilemma. I would like to see Matsushiro become a vibrant center of kosen-rufu from which happiness will spread throughout Japan.

"Nichiren Daishonin composed his treatise 'On Establishing the Correct Teaching for the Peace of the Land' in the wake of the great earthquake of 1257. He did so for the sake of the Japanese people, who were suffering from natural disasters, famine and epidemics. In the same way, I hope the members in Matsushiro will stand up for the well-being of their fellow citizens and transform their home into a realm of peace and tranquility. This is the struggle of the followers of Nichiren Daishonin."

Kuroki nodded in agreement and said: "I understand, and I will convey your exact words to our members in Matsushiro."

HEARING Akira Kuroki's reply, Shin'ichi Yamamoto sternly remarked: "If all you're going to do is convey my remarks, there's no need for you to go there. You might as well just send a letter or a telegram.

The purpose of leaders traveling to a local area, partici-pating in activities and meeting with members there is not simply to relay information. Please don't make that mistake.

"The purpose is to inspire members, change their per-spective and solidify their determination. Giving guid-ance in faith means to forge a life-to-life connection with the other person. If leaders go to the front lines of kosen-rufu with a halfhearted resolve, it's like fighting a losing battle."

Noticing Kuroki's tense and perplexed expression, Shin'ichi then remarked: "How do you change people's perspective? That's the question most on your mind, right?"

"Yes," Kuroki replied.

"The first step is for you, as the central figure, to de-termine in the depths of your being that you are going to build a great bastion of kosen-rufu in Matsushiro. You need to work toward this goal with the absolute convic-tion that you will not leave until you have accomplished it, or that you will die trying. Without such firm resolve, you cannot hope to open a new page in the history of kosen-rufu.

"The reason why I could achieve great victory in Osaka, Yamaguchi and everywhere else was that I always threw myself into the struggle with just such determina-tion. Half-serious efforts amount to nothing! Leaders who think only of maintaining their positions can never surmount incredible odds and come out triumphant. When you stand up on your own with a resolute mind and passionately call on others to join you, they are sure to stand up by your side.

"The German poet Goethe said: '*But never heart to heart will you be joining / Unless you let your own heart speak.*'[4] His words are so true. If leaders think that they can spur members to action with nothing more than dramatic pronouncements, they are extremely arrogant. Such people show nothing but disrespect toward others!"

With his gaze fixed on Shin'ichi, Kuroki decisively announced: "I will struggle with all my might and do my absolute best to completely transform all of Japan, starting with Matsushiro!"

SHIN'ICHI ROSE from his seat and placed his hand on Kuroki's shoulder. He then remarked with firmness: "That's it. That's the spirit you need. The members in Matsushiro have a strong love for their community, and their mission is as great as it is profound. They will certainly transform poison into medicine. I hope each of them will become a person their fellow citizens can rely and depend on, a person who is dedicated to protecting the welfare of the community. Now, in the face of this incredible adversity, it is time for the Matsushiro members to move boldly forward and realize tremendous victory.

"I would like to ask you to take some prayer bead cloths for the members from me and encourage them with all your might on my behalf."

Kuroki was deeply moved by Shin'ichi's warm consideration for those living in Matsushiro.

Kuroki arrived in Matsushiro on November 11 and attended a guidance meeting that evening at the home of Matsushiro District Leader Takeo Yamauchi. He said to all who had gathered: "President Yamamoto is very concerned about all of you here in Matsushiro. He is chanting for you every day. He also sent me with a gift of one thousand prayer bead cloths to give to you."

President Yamamoto's kindness left the members speechless. They were overwhelmed to think that even though he had never met them personally, he was so concerned about their well-being that he sent Headquarters Leader Kuroki to see them and present them with gifts of encouragement.

Stating that now was their opportunity to transform the destiny of Matsushiro, Kuroki then remarked: "In light of the principle of the oneness of life and its environment, transforming the destiny of the place where we reside requires nothing more than transforming our own destiny through doing our human revolution. Toward that end, let's stir up a great wave of propagation here in Matsushiro. And let's transform this community into a model realm of kosen-rufu!"

"The time is now. If we don't stand up now, when will we? I will take the lead in this struggle. Let's do it together!"

Enthusiastic cheers and applause reverberated throughout the room.

Lastly, Kuroki handed out the prayer bead cloths to everyone present. Tears filled many members' eyes as they received the gifts that they felt came directly from Shin'-ichi's heart.

AFTER THE MEETING, the members shared their thoughts with each other.

"I feel terrible that President Yamamoto has been worrying so much about us."

"I know what you mean. So let's chant in earnest and then go out and tell others about Buddhism. Let's create a Matsushiro that's brimming with happiness."

"Nichiren states, 'The reason that you have survived until now . . . was so that you would meet with this affair' (WND, 829). This is our crucial moment, so let's do our best."

With this determination, they joyfully set out to share Nichiren Daishonin's teachings with others.

When a strong fighting spirit burns in each person's heart, it becomes a great force for unprecedented advancement in kosen-rufu.

The very next day, November 12, saw members engaging in Buddhist dialogue all over town. The first person whose efforts bore fruit was a seventy-four-year-old member of the women's division. Inspired by this, all the members—young and old, men and women—initiated a friendly competition to spread the Mystic Law.

Up until then, the largest number of households to join the Soka Gakkai in Matsushiro in any given month was about fifteen. But through the members' efforts, in the space of a single day, some forty-five people had voiced a desire to give the practice a try.

In October, Matsushiro had been divided into three Soka Gakkai districts—Matsushiro, Kaizu and Higashijo. All three had now embarked on a new propagation effort in high spirits. This was an expression of the members' love for their community; their sincere wish to turn their home into a Land of Tranquil Light.

For several consecutive days starting from November 19, there were more than one hundred perceptible earthquakes per day. Seismologists could not determine whether this was a precursor to a big earthquake or if such medium-intensity quakes would simply continue to occur.

On November 26, the morning edition of the *Asahi Shimbun* newspaper ran a story with the headline, "Matsushiro Earthquakes Continue—'Knowledge' Wanted." The article related how a fact-finding group from the National Diet had asked the mayor of Matsushiro what the town needed most of all, and he had answered that while they needed many things, what they wanted most was knowledge or factual information.

The mayor's response betrayed a fervent desire to quell the residents' anxiety about what the future held.

THE *ASAHI SHIMBUN* article also mentioned the Clean Government Party and the Soka Gakkai, stating: "Whenever there is a quake, the Matsushiro Seismological Observatory is swamped with phone calls. Clean Government Party personnel are always among the first callers. The Clean Government Party was also the first to dispatch a fact-finding group of Diet members to the area, followed by the Japan Socialist Party and the Liberal Democratic Party, in that order.

"At the same time, the propagation activities of the Soka Gakkai, which is closely associated with the Clean Government Party, are increasing daily, and fifty new families have recently taken faith in Matsushiro."

The article went on to say that a growing number of people in the surrounding area were also joining the Soka Gakkai. In this way, the mass media showed keen interest in the members' dynamic propagation efforts.

Deeply resolved to transform the destiny of their

hometown and turn it into a realm of peace and tranquility, the Matsushiro members strove to infuse their community with the chanting of Nam-myoho-renge-kyo and to share Buddhism with as many of their fellow citizens as possible.

Shin'ichi Yamamoto also dispatched top Soka Gakkai leaders to Matsushiro to encourage the members there. On one occasion, Hiroshi Izumida, then vice general director, was sent. Attending a guidance meeting at the home of Matsushiro District Leader Takeo Yamauchi, he was astonished to see the enthusiasm of the members. Such a large number had gathered that many of them spilled out into the yard.

Izumida sat on a stool so that he could see everyone's face and began to speak: "The media has been making such a fuss about the earthquakes here that I thought the ground must be shaking constantly, but it's not so bad, is it? It seems the reports were somewhat exaggerated."

So far there hadn't been any major tremors that day, but no sooner had Izumida said this than the ground began to shake violently.

"Whoa!" cried Izumida as he toppled over on his stool. His face blanched with surprise. *So this is what they've been dealing with day after day*, he thought to himself as he lay there on the floor. *All right then! I'm going to encourage them with all I've got!* Once the shaking had subsided, he calmly stood up.

"I guess this shows that you cannot let your guard down, can you?" he remarked. At this, the members laughed heartily.

Izumida then said: "Nichiren Daishonin asserts, 'When

great evil occurs, great good follows' (WND, 1119). With determined prayer and courageous action, we can overcome any difficulty. Cherishing great hope in our hearts, let's transform all of our struggles into a springboard for tremendous advancement!'"

AS THE SEISMIC activity intensified, the Matsushiro members grew more vigorous.

Nichiren Buddhism offers various interpretations of the meaning of earthquakes. One is that they are a disaster manifesting as a result of people turning their backs on the correct teaching of Buddhism. Another is that they herald the flourishing of the correct teaching, as when the earth quaked and trembled in six different ways when Shakyamuni preached the Lotus Sutra. The members discussed these points in light of Nichiren's writings.

"If these earthquakes are the result of people turning their backs on the correct teaching, then fundamentally the only solution is for us to actively spread the Mystic Law. And if they are a sign of the flourishing of the correct teaching, then because our mission is to realize kosen-rufu, we need to strive to the best of our ability in that endeavor."

"All people have a right to become happy, so let's talk about Buddhism with everyone we know. Let's not leave a single person out of our efforts to share Nichiren's teachings!"

With this spirit, the Matsushiro members set out to meet with their friends and neighbors, unfazed by the shaking ground.

There were times when the mere mention of the Soka Gakkai resulted in doors being slammed in their faces or demands that they leave someone's property. But not even such negative treatment could impede their momentum. The more they took action, the more their hearts brimmed with a fighting spirit and a sense of joy to be working for their mission. Singing Soka Gakkai songs as they made their way through rice fields and along river embankments, they pressed forward cheerfully in their propagation efforts.

The vibrant attitudes and bright, confident smiles of these Soka Gakkai members gave courage to the citizens of Matsushiro, whose lives had become filled with anxiety and fear because of the earthquakes. Anxiety and fear can be contagious, but so can courage.

The earth continued to shake and tremble. There were 2,730 perceptible tremors recorded in November, 2,867 in December and 2,788 in January 1968. The first tremor to reach an intensity of five also occurred in January.

Numerous homes had tiles on their rooftops loosened from the quakes. Worried for their safety, parents told their children: "Don't rush outdoors during or soon after a tremor, and stay away from the sides of the streets where you can be struck by falling tiles."

Confused by this, the children would reply: "But if we walk in the middle of the street, we'll get hit by a car. So where should we walk?"

MANY HOMES also sustained cracks in their walls or more extensive damage from the earthquakes, and on cold winter days, freezing winds below minus fourteen degrees Fahrenheit blew in. Nevertheless, people refrained from using the kerosene stoves that they usually heated their homes with for fear of a fire breaking out. Instead, most families endured the cold huddling around more old-fashioned devices such as charcoal braziers or low tables with electric heat sources underneath. They kept buckets of water nearby in case of a fire.

While the tremors caused considerable damage to physical structures in the town, it was nothing compared to the mental and psychological toll they took on the local people. As the seismic activity continued, their fears grew that Mount Minakami would erupt. They lived in shaking houses that lacked sufficient heat to keep them warm from the cold. Terrified, they readied themselves to flee at a moment's notice, sleeping in their clothes with backpacks filled with emergency provisions next to their pillows.

All of these factors fueled the residents' anxiety and frustration, and many began to suffer from sleep deprivation, physical ailments and mental exhaustion. The tremors were having a psychological effect on the children as well. More and more, they were finding it difficult to concentrate on their studies, and many also said they were afraid and couldn't sleep.

Kerosene stoves were not used at Soka Gakkai gatherings, either. Some meeting places had charcoal braziers, but these weren't really enough to stave off the cold so members wore overcoats or padded quilt jackets indoors as well. But as they sang Soka Gakkai songs together and shared their experiences and determinations with each other, their lives overflowed with energy and warmth. As a result, their solidarity grew stronger.

Each time there was a tremor with an intensity of four or more, the police would send squad cars around to check for damage. For their part, Soka Gakkai district and group leaders would voluntarily go out to check on their fellow members after a big quake. They couldn't rest assured until they had seen with their own eyes that everyone was safe and sound. Even if a quake occurred in the middle of the night, they would carry flashlights and chant under their breath as they patrolled members' homes, some traveling by motorbike and others on foot.

Action is key. It is the great path of Soka.

If it appeared that everyone inside a home was sleeping undisturbed, the leaders would quietly check around the house for damage. Once they had confirmed that everything was fine there, they would move on to the next members' home.

IF THE LEADERS patrolling the neighborhood after a big earthquake saw that the lights were on in a member's home, they would stop in to make sure everything was all right and to inquire after the safety of the elderly and children. Cautioning the families about fires, they would also encourage them, saying: "Let's chant in earnest and overcome this ordeal together."

Before long, this network of support and encouragement expanded naturally to include not only Soka Gakkai members but all the residents living in Matsushiro.

Always working among the people, always reaching out to each individual—it is such steady efforts that become the driving force opening the way to the future.

On April 17, 1966, an astonishing 6,780 tremors were recorded in a single twenty-four-hour period. Of these, 661 were perceptible and three had an intensity of five. These strong quakes put cracks in the walls of almost every home in the area and caused clay tiles to fall from many rooftops. That night, afraid that their houses might collapse, several families took bedding out to the plastic greenhouses they used to grow vegetables and slept there.

Most homes had been reinforced with steel or wooden braces and had wooden cross supports covering their windows. Others had their clay tiles replaced with tin-plate. Among the local residents, some took refuge with relatives living outside the area. However, not knowing how long the tremors would continue, after a month or so, most of these families returned home again.

Shin'ichi Yamamoto received detailed reports about the enthusiastic activities being carried out by the Matsushiro members even amid their terrible living conditions. Wanting to encourage them to the fullest, at a Headquarters executive conference he proposed: "The Matsushiro members are really fighting hard in difficult circumstances. I'd like to suggest that we establish a community center there to give them hope. What do you think?" The leaders agreed that this was a wonderful idea.

Word of the new community center was relayed to the leaders in Matsushiro by telephone and then announced in the June 10 edition of the *Seikyo Shimbun*. The members were overjoyed at this great surprise. They immediately looked for an appropriate building for that purpose and at the same time stepped up their efforts to share Buddhism with others.

ONE MEMBER of the women's division decided that she would introduce her husband to the practice. She wished to do so for the simple reason that she wanted him to be protected from the ever-intensifying earthquakes. Her daughter, a second-year high school student, and her son, a third-year junior high school student, were both practicing diligently. They all wanted the father to join them. But he believed that life's fortunes and misfortunes came down to one's effort and convictions, and he didn't want to hear anything about Buddhism.

The family home was situated near a small mountain. On one occasion, a tremor sent a large boulder about three feet in diameter tumbling down into their yard. It grazed the house and settled in the garden, but at the same time the resultant landslide caused earth and gravel to come crashing through the wall of the drawing room. Fortunately, no one was hurt. The mother and children hugged each other and rejoiced that they had been protected. The father, however, startled by the sudden onslaught, sat in a daze. It was as if the boulder had broken through his hardened heart. When a member of the men's division visited the house not long after the accident, the father listened to what he had to say and agreed to start practicing.

Turning every obstacle into a springboard for the advancement of kosen-rufu—this was the spirit of the Matsushiro members.

In their search for a building that could be used as a Soka Gakkai community center, local leaders found a family that wanted to move out of their home. It was a two-story traditional wooden Japanese structure located in a quiet residential district on the south side of Matsushiro, where a number of old samurai dwellings still stood. The Soka Gakkai purchased the home on July 21.

That month also saw a major change in the seismic activity. In April, there had been more than 119,000 tremors, of which more than twelve thousand were perceptible. After that, however, they showed signs of decreasing, and in July they had declined dramatically to a total of 34,404 tremors, 2,756 of which were perceptible.

The members were overjoyed at this and started putting even greater effort into their propagation endeavors.

From August 1, as the ground continued shaking, construction to remodel the new community center began. Members used one room of the building to hold chanting sessions to pray that everything would be completed without incident.

SEISMIC ACTIVITY in Matsushiro had reached its peak in April and then declined through July, but it began to pick up again in August. With firm conviction in the Buddhist principles of the oneness of life and its environment and establishing the correct teaching for the peace of the land, the members put more energy into their efforts to share Buddhism with others determined to win.

Those who consistently burn with hope and boldly advance one step at a time are people of genuine faith.

The remodeling of the new Matsushiro Community Center proceeded smoothly and, on August 24, the opening ceremony took place. It was the fifth Soka Gakkai community center in Nagano Prefecture. Members attended the ceremony in high spirits, filled with great resolve to transform their beloved community into a shining citadel of happiness. One such individual was a young men's member who had introduced eight families to Buddhism that month.

August 24 was also Shin'ichi Yamamoto's anniversary of joining the Soka Gakkai. From Tokyo, he strengthened his determination to take an even more dynamic role in leading the kosen-rufu movement, and prayed wholeheartedly for Matsushiro's prosperity and that the earthquakes would abate as quickly as possible.

The establishment of the new community center gave fresh impetus to the Matsushiro members' fighting spirit, and their propagation activities increased even further.

By the day of the opening ceremony, the total number of tremors recorded since the outbreak exceeded five hundred thousand, of which more than forty-eight thousand were perceptible. In September, there was a landslide in the Makiuchi district of Matsushiro, and eleven homes and other structures were completely destroyed. Meanwhile, water springing up through earthquake-induced cracks in the ground was also causing great damage. In the autumn, the seismic activity began to spread from Matsushiro to neighboring areas such as Koshoku City and Kamiyamada Town.

At the Headquarters leaders meeting held in January of the following year, 1967, a chapter was finally established in Matsushiro. With this, the members' determination burned even brighter. In February, the traditional month of propagation in the Soka Gakkai, the Headquarters announced a goal of one new member-household for each group. The newly formed Matsushiro Chapter thus initiated a great struggle to achieve that target before any other chapter in Japan.

The February 27 issue of the *Seikyo Shimbun* carried the names of the chapters that had achieved the propagation goal for that month. Among them, the name of Matsushiro Chapter, having realized brilliant victory in its first campaign as a chapter, shone proudly on the page.

AFTER MATSUSHIRO Chapter was formed, it became a fervent desire of the local members to welcome President Yamamoto to their town. They wanted him to see just how energetic and positive they were despite having to live with constant earthquakes. Their wish finally came true five months later, on June 23, with Shin'ichi's visit to Matsushiro.

Shin'ichi took the train from Ueno Station in Tokyo and arrived at Komoro Station in Nagano Prefecture just after noon. At the advice of Nagano Joint Headquarters Leader Yukio Akaishi, he made a visit to Kaikoen Park, built on the ruins of Komoro Castle. Akaishi was a good-natured man in his forties who had received encouragement and training from Shin'ichi since his youth. About fourteen years earlier, when Shin'ichi was the leader of the young men's division First Corps, Akaishi was also a leader of the corps while at the same time serving as a group leader in the line organization. Akaishi was having difficulty fulfilling his responsibilities in both leadership positions as well as his job and had begun to feel that it was all too much for him to handle.

After thinking about it for some time, he decided to resign from his position as a young men's leader. He wrote a letter of resignation and after a meeting handed it to Shin'ichi.

Shin'ichi knew Akaishi's character very well. He knew he was a sincere person, but was quick to give in to his weaknesses and throw in the towel before trying his hardest. *Unless he broke through that inner obstacle now,* Shin'ichi thought, he *would end up living a life of defeat without ever having really struggled.*

A victor is just another name for someone who has overcome his or her own weaknesses.

Shin'ichi looked Akaishi straight in the eye and said: "So, you're running away?"

Akaishi trembled with nervousness. He felt as if Shin'-ichi had pierced through his inner darkness.

In a lightly chiding tone, Shin'ichi continued: "There's nothing to worry about. Just chant with your whole heart and do your absolute best in every endeavor without giving up. If you do, you are sure to triumph. I will support you."

He then tore up Akaishi's letter of resignation. "We're settled now, right?" he said and smiled warmly as he left the room.

SHIN'ICHI UNDERSTOOD Yukio Akaishi's feelings and worries only too well. He could just as easily have accepted Akaishi's resignation and appeased him, saying, "It must be very hard to be so busy with two leadership positions. Why don't you take a little break?" But if he had done that, he would only have been encouraging Akaishi's inherent weakness that made him want to run away at the first sign of difficulty.

We grow when we push ourselves beyond our limitations, when we challenge ourselves to go further than we think we can. By doing so, we can break through our shell, become strong, expand our state of life and carry out our human revolution. This is the way of Buddhist practice.

Hence came Shin'ichi's decision to nudge Akaishi forward. Akaishi, however, was at first stunned. Shin'ichi's declaration, "So, you're running away?" made him realize that he shouldn't quit, but at the same time, he had no idea what to do about his situation. Nor was he confident in his ability to fulfill his duties. Akaishi wanted to speak to Shin'ichi again, but he was hesitant. He was afraid that if he were to ask for guidance, Shin'ichi would scold him for continuing to waver.

But he mustered his courage and headed for Shin'-ichi's apartment in Sanno in Tokyo's Ota Ward. Shin'-ichi's wife, Mineko, answered the door.

"I'm sorry for troubling you so late," Akaishi apologized, "but I was hoping that I could receive some guidance from Mr. Yamamoto."

Shin'ichi's voice came from inside: "I've been expecting you. Let's go to the public bath together."

Mineko gave each of them a towel and soap, and the two men headed out. Shin'ichi draped his towel around his neck and whistled a tune as they strolled along. Akaishi followed behind in silence. The moon and stars shone brightly in the night sky.

Akaishi was well aware that Shin'ichi carried several different responsibilities simultaneously, including sales manager at Josei Toda's company, young men's corps leader, national leader in charge of training youth leaders and acting leader of Bunkyo Chapter. He was amazed at how calm Shin'ichi always seemed in spite of these heavy demands.

PERHAPS because of the late hour, the public bath was almost empty. As they sat soaking in the big tub, Yukio Akaishi said to Shin'ichi Yamamoto: "You have so many different responsibilities and are far busier than I am. How is it that you are always so calm and collected?"

"Do I seem calm and collected?" Shin'ichi asked.

Akaishi nodded.

"If I appear that way, it's because I am completely committed to what I'm doing. I'm in a position that requires me to be on my toes every moment. I need to ensure that Mr. Toda can initiate an everlasting current of kosen-rufu while he is alive. To do that, the Soka Gakkai cannot afford any missteps or defeats. It is my responsibility to see that everything is successfully carried through.

"If we were to suffer defeat, Mr. Toda's vision of kosen-rufu would collapse. I have firmly resolved not to be the kind of disciple who would allow his mentor's plans to fail. A disciple who would let that happen is ultimately nothing more than a 'parasite in the lion's bowels.'

"That's why I mustn't fail. It's my destiny to win. If you are absolutely determined to win and pray wholeheartedly for that result, then courage, wisdom and strength will well forth from the depths of your being."

Akaishi nodded thoughtfully as he listened to Shin'ichi speak.

"If you are passive and simply follow instructions, your life will be dull and stagnant. You will be no more than a slave to your circumstances. But if you take the initiative and courageously rise to every challenge you encounter, you are living the life of a champion. Your life-condition will soar and you will experience boundless joy.

"Depending on whether you take an active or passive approach, though your day-to-day activities remain the same, you will feel an enormous difference in your inner commitment and sense of personal fulfillment. And naturally you will see results. As long as you are going to participate in Soka Gakkai activities, I hope you will do so as a leading protagonist, boldly taking action in a way that suits you."

Looking at Akaishi, Shin'ichi smiled and stretched his arms and legs out in the bath. "Ah, this feels great."

Akaishi stretched his limbs, too. Talking with Shin'ichi caused his tension to dissipate and he felt a burst of fresh energy surge throughout his body.

AFTER THEIR BATH, the two men returned to Shin'ichi's apartment.

Continuing to encourage Akaishi, Shin'ichi said: "The task of realizing kosen-rufu is the responsibility of the youth division. It is an undertaking accomplished by developing yourself as a youth division member, performing your duties to the best of your ability and living out your life with youthful vigor.

"Youth is a time of challenge, a time of seeing all your endeavors through to the end without giving up. That's how you forge and strengthen yourself, build fortune and achieve great development.

"Let's give our all to working for kosen-rufu. Let's struggle together. Let's devote ourselves fully to our goal. It doesn't matter if no one else sees your efforts; the Gohonzon knows everything."

Shin'ichi then suggested that they listen to some music and put on a record. The buoyant melody of Franz von Suppé's *Light Cavalry Overture* filled the room.

"It's uplifting, isn't it?" Shin'ichi asked. "No matter how busy we are, we need to relax and listen to music once in a while. Practicing Buddhism isn't about cutting ourselves off from the rest of life. Kosen-rufu is ultimately a movement to create a truly humanistic culture and way of life."

Next Shin'ichi played Beethoven's *Fifth Symphony*. The powerful rhythms of Beethoven reverberated in Akaishi's heart, and he felt courage welling forth from the depths of his life, as if in time to the music. When they finished listening to the record, Akaishi said: "Thank you very much. I'll do my best!"

Shin'ichi smiled gently and nodded as he remarked: "No matter how frustrated or sad you might feel at times, or what difficulties you may face, it's important to always keep moving forward. Beethoven wrote of finding 'joy through suffering.' If you can advance beyond your suffering, you will experience the clear skies of joy and victory stretching far and wide above you. When you think of it that way, even hardship is enjoyable!"

"I see what you mean!" Akaishi replied with spirit.

Akaishi walked home from Shin'ichi's place with a light step and a heart filled with fresh determination. He found himself gazing up at the moon and singing a Soka Gakkai song softly to himself. This was a major turning point in his life.

YUKIO AKAISHI eventually became a central leader of the young men's division and then a top leader of Nagano Prefecture. When he took on the latter responsibility, Shin'ichi Yamamoto composed a poem for him. On the flyleaf of a book, Shin'ichi wrote:

> You, too, will grow magnificently
> into a brave champion,
> supporting the Gakkai
> and devoting yourself to kosen-rufu
> until the last moment of your life.

Now Akaishi, as the leader of Nagano Joint Headquarters, was working actively with his fellow members in Nagano, a region renowned for its natural beauty.

Built on the ruins of Komoro Castle, Kaikoen Park contains a museum dedicated to the writer Toson Shimazaki[5] and a zoo. Strolling around the park with Shin'ichi, Akaishi and the other local leaders were overjoyed to finally be able to welcome him to Nagano. When they thought of how happy the Matsushiro members would be in particular, they felt a surge of emotion rising in their hearts. They had been making every effort to support and encourage the members there during the long series of earthquakes.

A park employee who was guiding them said: "The birds are really singing today." Sure enough, the group then noticed the cheerful, high-pitched—and at times even raucous—birdsong that was echoing from the treetops.

Further on they came upon a large cage with peacocks in it. When Shin'ichi approached more closely, two of the birds spread their tails in wide, shimmering fans of color. To Akaishi and the others, it seemed as if everything around them was welcoming Shin'ichi to their homeland.

After their brief tour of Kaikoen Park, the group headed for the Soka Gakkai's Komoro Community Center by car. After reciting the sutra and chanting Nam-myoho-renge-kyo with representative members there, they went to Matsushiro.

Shin'ichi wanted to meet as many people as possible and inspire them to stand up in faith throughout their lives. *This day will never come again. How many people can I encourage before it is over?* With this thought, Shin'ichi was determined not to waste a single moment.

What can I do now? What did I accomplish today? Kosen-rufu is a struggle against the limits of time.

Shin'ichi arrived at the Matsushiro Community Center at half past three in the afternoon. The members had gathered in such numbers that the meeting room was overflowing. Instead of going through the main entrance of the building, Shin'ichi went around to the side veranda, took off his shoes there and entered the room directly. He couldn't wait another moment to see the members and encourage them with all his might.

"Hello! I'm here at last!" his voice rang out.

WHEN THE MEMBERS heard Shin'ichi Yamamoto's voice, their faces lit up and they broke into excited cheers and applause. A spirited recitation of the evening prayers commenced. Just then, a rumbling sound echoed from the earth and there was a loud boom as the ground heaved upward and started to shake. A moment of tension filled the room, but everyone continued to chant earnestly, their voices resonating as one.

When the evening prayers were finished, Shin'ichi turned around and commented to the members sitting in the front row: "Since becoming president of the Soka Gakkai, I have prayed that there would be no earthquakes and that Japan would always have bountiful harvests. I will continue praying for that. Let's overcome every hardship and disaster with firm resolve and strong prayer."

After Katsu Kiyohara and Hiroshi Izumida delivered greetings to the members, it was Shin'ichi's turn to speak. He said: "I am overjoyed to see you all today looking so vibrant and well. Now, what is our mission? It is to establish the correct teaching for the peace of the land—to build, based on Nichiren Daishonin's teachings, a peaceful and secure society free of calamity and war.

"What is the correct teaching? In his treatise 'On

Establishing the Correct Teaching for the Peace of the Land,' Nichiren urges us to take faith in 'the one true vehicle, the single good doctrine' (WND, 25); in other words, the Lotus Sutra. The Lotus Sutra is a teaching of the fundamental Law of life permeating the entire universe; it expounds the philosophy of respect for life and the principle of compassion.

"Nichiren Daishonin declares that by making the correct teaching the basis of our lives and transforming our minds and our life tendency, we can change our external circumstances and build indestructible happiness. This is possible because the self and the surrounding environment are essentially interconnected, a concept elucidated by the Buddhist principle of the oneness of life and its environment.

"In other words, all phenomena in the universe are encompassed within one's own life and, at the same time, one's life pervades the entire universe. That is why we can change any situation with our faith and earnest efforts. This is a fundamental tenet of Buddhism. Therefore, no matter what happens, we needn't become discouraged. If we become weak and lose our momentum, we will be defeated.

"I hope you will act with courage. Courage is strength. Courage is wisdom. It is the driving force for victory."

SHIN'ICHI CONTINUED: "Nichiren Daishonin writes: 'The time will come when all people will ... take up the single vehicle of Buddhahood, and the Mystic Law alone will flourish throughout the land. When the people all chant Nam-myoho-renge-kyo, the wind will no longer buffet the branches, and the rain will no longer break the clods of soil' (wnd, 392). In other words, when people everywhere have faith in the Mystic Law, the fundamental Law of life, and chant Nam-myoho-renge-kyo, they will not suffer from natural disasters. We should all have great conviction in Nichiren Daishonin's words.

"That's why our aim is kosen-rufu. When people far and wide start to practice Nichiren Buddhism, and the philosophy of compassion and the sanctity of life become the foundation of human society, the protection of human beings and all other life forms will become a top priority. At that time, sufficient effort will be allocated to developing the technology for predicting and even preventing earthquakes, as well as to establishing proper emergency measures if they do occur. At last, the construction of a safe and secure society will become possible. The role of government is also extremely important toward this end.

"At any rate, the mission of Buddhist practitioners is to strive to find a solution to humanity's suffering. Matsushiro is the place where, during World War II, the military government planned to transfer the Imperial Headquarters in preparation for a ground war on Japanese soil, and today it is a land plagued by earthquake swarms. From the standpoint of Buddhism, you have all gathered here as emissaries of the Buddha in order to transform Matsushiro's destiny and make it a 'safe and tranquil' realm as taught in the Lotus Sutra (ls, 230).

"Matsushiro is the grand stage of your mission. I hope

you will exert yourselves to the fullest extent of your ability here. The fact is that times of suffering and hardship are an opportunity to achieve wonderful growth and accumulate tremendous good fortune. If you stand up and face the challenge at such times, you can adorn your life with everlasting benefit. But if you are cowardly, you will regret it throughout your life.

"I hope that all of you, my dear fellow members in Matsushiro, will initiate a great struggle! Please create a model organization that the rest of Japan will want to emulate and achieve victory in our second round of kosen-rufu."

Resounding applause that conveyed the members' unwavering commitment shook the room.

SHIN'ICHI NEXT DISCUSSED what is necessary to lead a strong and correct life and build happiness: "The important thing is to maintain faith in the Gohonzon throughout your life, and to always practice with the Soka Gakkai, the true harmonious community of practitioners of Nichiren Buddhism. People cannot exist in a vacuum. Alone, people tend to become weak. That is why, in order to construct a life of indestructible happiness, we need good-hearted fellow members and an organization to help us deepen and persevere in faith.

"From that point of view, it becomes clear just how wonderful it is to practice within the Soka Gakkai, the organization that has inherited and is carrying on Nichiren's spirit. Nevertheless, there are some people who are always ready to complain and grumble about something, saying things like: 'Soka Gakkai activities are too demanding,' or 'I don't like so-and-so.' Of course, no one in Matsushiro is like that!"

When Shin'ichi said this, the audience burst into laughter.

He continued: "Actually, such complaints and faultfinding end up erasing whatever benefits and good fortune you have acquired in the course of your practice. They also rob you of joy and cause you to feel miserable, ultimately rendering you the creator of your own unhappiness. On the other hand, a positive, appreciative attitude makes your joy multiply, and leads to personal fulfillment and happiness.

"Where there is joy, strength increases and energy grows. Victory in life and in kosen-rufu is found in such joyful advance. In other words, the results we gain from chanting to the Gohonzon and engaging in Soka Gakkai activities will be completely different depending upon whether our attitude is positive or negative.

"I hope that all of you will devote yourselves to your practice with appreciation and joy, so that you may continue to accumulate great good fortune."

Everyone applauded and called out enthusiastically in agreement.

Lastly, Shin'ichi said: "I will come again and again to encourage you, my fellow members in Nagano. Let's continue our struggle together!"

The members felt as if a refreshing breeze had blown through their hearts, filling them with courage.

FROM THE Matsushiro Community Center, local members took Shin'ichi Yamamoto to see the ancient battlefield of Kawanakajima. Kawanakajima (literally, "Island Between Rivers") refers to the alluvial fan between the Sai and Chikuma rivers at the Zenkojidaira basin. It is known as the site of frequent battles among the armies of sixteenth-century warlords Takeda Shingen of Kai Province (modern Yamanashi Prefecture) and Uesugi Kenshin of Echigo Province (modern Niigata Prefecture).

When Shin'ichi and the others arrived there, local young men's members brought out a diagram showing the topography of the area as well as the battle formations of the opposing forces, and explained the battles.

Five major battles took place at Kawanakajima. During the fourth, which occurred in September 1561, the two feudal lords engaged in direct combat. A statue depicting that encounter was erected at a place called Hachimanbara in Kawanakajima. Looking at the statue, Shin'ichi reflected on the bitter struggle between these two mighty generals. He imagined that their soldiers must have been galvanized at the sight of their commanders engaged in such a decisive fight.

Nichiren Daishonin writes: "In battles soldiers regard the general as their soul. If the general were to lose heart, his soldiers would become cowards" (WND, 613). Victory or defeat depends on the resolve and courage of leaders.

Shin'ichi recalled singing "The Mists of Kawanakajima," a song paying tribute to the fight between the two generals, in front of his mentor Josei Toda as if it were just yesterday. It was August 1957, about a month after a tentative conclusion had been reached in the Yubari Coal

Miners Union Incident,[6] in which union leaders threatened Soka Gakkai members' religious freedom. The members' emotions were still running high.

Around that time, a celebration marking the completion of a new temple in Yubari was held, and it was there that Shin'ichi sang "The Mists of Kawanakajima" for President Toda.

> *There are no sounds of men or horses,*
> *and even the grass droops low*
> *in the heavy mist of Kawanakajima.*

Toda made Shin'ichi sing the song over and over, tears filling his eyes as he listened. All of a sudden, he shouted out with rage: "The leaders of the Coal Miners Union are cowards! When I'm not here, they try to run roughshod over my dear disciples. Then when I come, they don't show their faces! Let them bring their charges to me directly! I will never flee or hide! The precious members are my life!"

Toda would not stand for injustice. As long as there was breath in his body, he would take the lead and fight to the very end—this was the firm determination of Josei Toda, a man dedicated to working for the happiness of the people.

AUGUST 1957 was only seven months before Toda's death. His health was already dangerously frail. Nevertheless, determined to protect the members, he traveled all the way to Yubari in Hokkaido to confront the union leaders and settle things once and for all. He was indeed a great champion of tremendous courage who was willing to give his life for his beliefs.

No doubt afraid of coming face-to-face with such a leader, the union officials, who had initiated the confrontation with the Soka Gakkai in the first place, didn't even show themselves despite knowing that Toda was in Yubari.

The third verse of "The Mists of Kawanakajima" contains the lines:

> *In the midst of the continuous onslaught,*
> *sadly, the enemy general escaped.*

These lyrics express the bitter chagrin felt by Uesugi Kenshin at the escape of his opponent, Takeda Shingen, and they exactly echoed Toda's sentiments. That was the reason for his vehement remarks about the union leaders. His voice on that day still rang in Shin'ichi's ears.

There are no easy battles in the great struggle for kosen-rufu. Halfhearted determination and actions will invite terrible defeat. Toda wanted to teach his disciples that justice and victory for humanity could only be achieved with strong conviction and the tenacity to carry out a bold and valiant struggle against iniquity.

On the evening of his visit to Matsushiro, Shin'ichi chanted sincerely in his room at the inn where he was staying for the earthquake swarm to cease. Thinking of the local residents fearing for their lives in homes with cracked walls, his heart ached. He couldn't help but pray with all his might.

At about this time, it was believed that the Matsushiro

earthquakes had passed their peak, but the tremors in the adjoining regions continued unabated and there was no telling whether they would subside. People remained concerned, but little by little the seismic activity died down. At last on July 7, for the first time in twenty-two months, there were no perceptible earthquakes.

From then on, the number of tremors gradually declined until finally they ceased altogether. As the Matsushiro members strove through their faith to overcome the difficulty of living with the earthquakes, their sense of being the protectors of their community deepened. Their dedicated efforts to encourage and support their fellow citizens created a strong bond of trust that contributed greatly to the expansion of kosen-rufu in the area.

ON THE FOLLOWING DAY, June 24, Shin'ichi attended a commemorative photo session for Nagano Joint Headquarters in Matsumoto City, Nagano Prefecture. It was his first visit to the city in seven years. The last time had been in November 1960, the year he became Soka Gakkai president, when he attended a meeting there marking the establishment of Matsumoto Chapter.

The day after that 1960 Matsumoto meeting, Shin'ichi had gone to Nagano City to attend a meeting for the establishment of Nagano Chapter. Those two inauguration gatherings were the beginning of the long journey of kosen-rufu for Shin'ichi and the Nagano members.

Now, seven years later, the local members were overjoyed to make a fresh departure together with President

Yamamoto at the beginning of the second round of kosen-rufu. To add to their excitement, they were going to have their photo taken with Shin'ichi, a memento that would serve as an everlasting record of their determination.

The faces of the four thousand men's and women's group leaders who had gathered in the hall for the photo session shone with happiness and pride. In the distance, Mount Norikura, Mount Hotaka and the other peaks of the Northern Japan Alps rose into the clear sky. The shoot started at two o'clock in the afternoon and was carried out in fifteen sessions.

Gazing at the faces of the members standing on the bleachers, Shin'ichi began speaking to them. To one member he said: "Please take care of your health. In order to continue making your best effort, it's vital that you never neglect your health." To another he remarked: "Do your best every day so that you have no regrets! Regrets are a source of unhappiness." And to another: "We are now at a critical juncture in our endeavor for kosen-rufu. Without determined struggle, there can be no victory!"

Shin'ichi's powerful words inspired fresh resolve in the hearts of the Nagano members to set out anew. With that thought in mind, they had their pictures taken with President Yamamoto. They eagerly looked forward to seeing the developed photographs.

"Oh, no!" cried Takeshi Yaguruma, head of the *Seikyo Shimbun* photography division, as he worked in the darkroom at the newspaper building. He had just placed the film for the commemorative photo session at Matsumoto in the developer and touched the liquid with his finger. It was too warm. He had left the hot water he was using to heat the developer bath running too long.

He quickly removed the film. The developer bath should have been sixty-eight degrees Fahrenheit. When the bath was too warm, the film's emulsion layer could expand and soften, causing reticulation and other effects that would spoil the film's development.

THE FINISHED ROLLS of film from each of the photo sessions that Shin'ichi Yamamoto had taken with members around Japan were sent to the *Seikyo Shimbun* head office in Tokyo to be developed. Takeshi Yaguruma bore full responsibility for these photo sessions, which had been initiated by Shin'ichi two years earlier, in 1965. There were times when a single session might involve as many as twenty-four thousand members being photographed in fifty groups, but until now nothing had ever gone wrong.

Yaguruma consistently told himself that each photograph was a precious memory that members would cherish all their lives, and as such he could not afford even one error. He therefore made a conscious effort to approach every task with fresh awareness. However, as he became used to his work, his attention began to slacken and he grew lax. Laxity breeds carelessness. Now he had failed to observe the most basic step of film developing—that of checking the temperature of the developer before placing in the film. It was a mistake caused by a single moment's negligence.

Life and kosen-rufu can both be described as a ceaseless struggle against our inner lethargy and carelessness.

The enemy is not outside; it resides within our own hearts. To realize victory, then, it is crucial that we defeat the negative workings in the depths of our lives.

Yaguruma turned off the hot water he was using to heat the chemicals and turned on the cold. This time he checked the temperature with his finger and, while chanting silently, went through the rest of the development process. Illuminated by the green light of the darkroom, his face was wrought with tension, his brow furrowed in concern. When the film processing was completed, he checked the final product. The portion that had been in the overheated developer was, as he had anticipated, damaged. When he made a print, creases in the film's emulsion blurred the image.

A chill ran down his spine, and his legs felt like they might buckle, but he summoned his strength and stepped out of the darkroom. With the color drained from his face, he said to the other staff members of the photography division: "I've just made a terrible mistake." When he told them what had happened, they were all at a loss for words.

THE PHOTOGRAPHY division staff members were well aware of the trouble President Yamamoto went through to make time in his schedule for commemorative photos with members working on the front lines of kosen-rufu. They also knew how much members around Japan looked forward to these opportunities and the effort they put into making special arrangements at work or at home in order to participate. That is why the staff members keenly understood that the matter would not end with the simple admission of a mistake having been made.

They began exploring every possible means of reproducing the image. Their best hope, they decided, was to make a print as large as a newspaper page and try to correct the blurred area by hand with a fine brush, and then make a copy negative by photographing the retouched photo.

Yaguruma explained the situation to *Seikyo Shimbun* Managing Editor Susumu Aota and discussed what course of action they should take. It was such a grave matter that Aota broke out in a cold sweat as he considered the alternatives. After much deliberation, it was finally decided that they would put their efforts into retouching the image. They then showed it to a technician at a well-known photo lab who examined it and said: "We may be able to do something about this." Placing their last ray of hope in those words, they asked him to do his best.

The job took about a month. The finished product, however, was obviously retouched. The eyebrows and eyes of some of the members in the photo stood out with unnatural clarity, and others' faces were barely recognizable. Yaguruma was made painfully aware of the serious outcome that could result from a moment's carelessness. But there is no point in regretting what is past; we cannot turn back the clock.

Yaguruma traveled to the head temple, where the annual summer training course was taking place, in order to show the photograph to President Yamamoto. Filled with trepidation, he handed the photo to Shin'ichi, who was sitting in a tent set up in front of the Grand Reception Hall, saying: "This is the Nagano Joint Headquarters commemorative photo."

Shin'ichi looked at the image. In the next instant, his eyes flashed in anger and he sternly asked: "What happened to this photograph?"

"I'm terribly sorry!" Yaguruma apologized, bowing low as he explained his error.

SHIN'ICHI WAS GRATEFUL for the hard work Yaguruma and the other staff members of the *Seikyo Shimbun* photography division put into the entire commemorative photo project. That's what made this slipup even more regrettable.

As he listened to Yaguruma's explanation, Shin'ichi saw that it was the result of a moment's negligence. But such moments can cause irreparable damage. That is the harsh reality of life. A famous proverb says that a thousand days of brilliant achievement can be erased in a single instant. There are cases too numerous to mention of people who accomplished wonderful things, only to have them destroyed by a slight act of carelessness. In every endeavor, true victors are those who never relax their guard, remain strict with themselves and continue challenging themselves to the very end.

Shin'ichi's tone was stern as he spoke: "There are many factors that led to your mistake, but at the core of them all is arrogance. The members regard these photographs as a great treasure of their life. You can imagine how disappointed they will be if the images are ruined. While this may be at the top of your mind at the outset, if you grow complacent, you will eventually stop view-ing it seriously. You then start to take your job lightly, thinking that since you've come so far without making a mistake, everything will be fine. In other words, you be-come overconfident.

"Such arrogance is sure to lead to your own downfall as well as that of the Soka Gakkai. I am struggling with all my might. Halfhearted people are nothing but a hin-drance and a bother!"

Shin'ichi considered Yaguruma to be a precious and trusted disciple. He therefore didn't want him to con-tinue making errors that would lead to his defeat in life. That is why he was so hard on him.

Yaguruma felt tears of bitter regret and shame welling up in his eyes.

Shin'ichi's guidance not only stung him but also sharply awakened all the photography division staff members in charge of the commemorative photo ses-sions to the spirit they should have.

SEVERAL DAYS later, Takeshi Yaguruma learned that Shin'ichi Yamamoto had voiced a desire to re-turn to Nagano and retake the commemorative photos. Yaguruma felt a mix of relief and tension.

In October, four months after his visit to Matsushiro, Shin'ichi's wish was realized. Photo sessions were sched-uled over two days—in Shiojiri City on October 7, and Nagano City on October 8. Around this time, Shin'ichi had been burning the candle at both ends preparing for a number of activities surrounding the groundbreaking ceremony for the Grand Main Temple that was to be held on October 12. These included overseeing preliminary meetings for the event as well as composing the manuscript to be read on the occasion of the official vow to build the Grand Main Temple. In the midst of all this, Shin'ichi went to Nagano to reshoot the commemorative photos.

When Shin'ichi arrived on the morning of October 7 at the Soka Gakkai Suwa Community Center in Suwa City, Nagano, he was so exhausted that he needed the support of the leaders traveling with him just to walk. But having come that far, he was not about to turn back.

It is by summoning every ounce of our strength and exerting ourselves completely to take even one more step forward that we can construct a brilliant record of achievement.

At the community center, Shin'ichi recited the sutra and chanted Nam-myoho-renge-kyo with those who had accompanied him from Tokyo, praying with all his might for great energy to emerge from the depths of his life. Yaguruma was among the people traveling with Shin'ichi. He felt terrible that it was his mistake that had caused Shin'ichi to have to retake the photos.

When they entered the venue where the shoot was to be held, they found the members in high spirits at having another opportunity to meet with President Yamamoto. Shin'ichi appeared before the members exuding vigor and energy. "Thank you for coming!" he said. "The photographs we took earlier were spoiled, so we had to ask you to come again. I'm so sorry. But this time I promise there will be no problems."

He then pointed to Yaguruma standing behind the

camera and said lightheartedly: "He's the one who made the mistake last time. If he does it again, I'll have to fire him, don't you think?"

Everyone laughed. It was a warm laughter filled with joy at this second encounter with Shin'ichi. A heavy weight seemed to lift from Yaguruma's shoulders. In the viewfinder, he saw the brilliant smiles of the children of the Buddha. In the next instant, the image was blurred by his own tears. Yaguruma pressed the shutter with intense concentration.

IN THE INTERVAL between sessions, Shin'ichi quietly slipped out of the gymnasium where the photography was taking place. He had felt short of breath and wanted to get some fresh air and rest a bit. When he did so, a *Seikyo Shimbun* photographer, who had been watching his every move intently, followed after him.

Wherever Shin'ichi went, a moving drama of human encounter seemed to unfold. Photographers and reporters for the newspaper therefore did their utmost not to miss even one of those moments.

When the photographer stepped outside, he saw Shin'ichi sitting alone on some concrete steps. It was clear that he was exhausted. He looked as if he might be crushed under the accumulated fatigue of his hard schedule.

Sensing the photographer's presence, Shin'ichi looked in his direction and remarked with a slight smile: "Ah, you caught me off guard. I really shouldn't let my weariness show."

Taking a deep breath, he then mustered his strength and said: "Right! Let's go!" He then walked briskly back into the gymnasium.

When the members standing on the bleachers saw him, they greeted him with a storm of applause.

"Thank you!" he called out. "Thank you so much for your hard work. I hope you will all relax today." His voice was vigorous. "I have received detailed reports about your courageous activities and great achievements, and I am well aware of your efforts. Kosen-rufu is an eternal struggle. Therefore, no matter what happens, it's important to continue carrying it through. If you failed yesterday, then win today. If you were defeated today, then win tomorrow. And if you won yesterday and today, make sure you keep doing so.

"The life force of the Buddha pulses dynamically in our unceasing efforts to work hard for the happiness of others. It is in such action that we experience boundless joy and that the great path to indestructible happiness is opened. Let us all begin our struggle anew from today! Let us start on a fresh, hope-filled advance!"

Shin'ichi's words rang with the force of a lion's roar. His travels to meet with and encourage members constituted an arduous struggle with himself.

SHIN'ICHI'S CONSTANT desire was to search out members who were diligently struggling under the most challenging circumstances and praise and encourage them. For that reason, he aimed to visit not only big cities but small towns and villages as well. Meeting and encouraging all the members he wanted to in a limited amount of time made doing so rather difficult. Still, whenever possible, he adjusted his schedule so that he could go to those outlying areas.

His trip to Komoro and Matsushiro in Nagano Prefecture back on June 23 was one such visit, and nine days before that he had gone to Hikone in Shiga Prefecture. In July, he had traveled to the Kyushu, Chubu and Tohoku regions, and from July 24, he participated in the annual summer training course at the head temple. The course finished on August 11, and from the following day he traveled to Hyogo, Fukui and Toyama prefectures. On August 15, the anniversary of the end of World War II, he went to Takayama City in Gifu Prefecture to visit the Soka Gakkai Takayama Community Center.

Takayama was a beautiful, serene city surrounded by lush, green mountains. It was in February of the previous year, 1966, that Shin'ichi had decided to go there. At that time, he had been participating in a commemorative photo session with local members at the Gifu Community Center in Gifu City, and a member of the women's division from Takayama had entreated him to visit the city. Her voice rang with such earnestness that Shin'ichi had replied on the spot: "Yes, I promise!"

He then asked the local leaders what life was like in Takayama. They explained that the Hida area, where Takayama was located, while known for its stunning scenery, was rather inaccessible. The main industries were forestry and woodworking, and the local economy was in dire straits. Many of the members there were experiencing financial hardship, they said.

Coming to a quick decision, Shin'ichi remarked: "If that's the case, then let's establish a community center in Takayama to make it easier for the members to do Gakkai activities. I would like our Hida members to become models of how to transform one's karma and to send the winds of happiness blowing all across Japan."

When leaders respond promptly to the voice of the people, everyone advances with joy and hope.

THOUGH SHIN'ICHI Yamamoto could not immediately find the time to go to Takayama, whenever he thought of the members there he chanted for them. Meanwhile, preparations for the establishment of a Soka Gakkai community center in the city got under way with the purchase of a two-story private home and its subsequent remodeling. And in October of the previous year, 1966, the Takayama Community Center—a

shining citadel of kosen-rufu— finally opened in Takayama City, the leading city of the Hida area.

Now on his visit to the region on August 15, Shin'ichi
was met at Takayama Station and driven to the community center by a local youth member. Mount Norikura,
Mount Hotaka and other peaks of the Northern Japan
Alps rose through the thin layer of clouds in the sky. The
Hida region, comprised of Takayama City and the three
counties of Yoshiki, Ono and Mashita, was an isolated,
mountainous area that became blanketed in deep snow
in the winter.

The people of Hida were simple, honest and hard-
working, but they were living in a place that had long
suffered from poverty. The region's history was one of
the hardship and struggle of ordinary people, as well as
their victory and triumph. In the Genroku era[7] of the
feudal Edo period, Hida, with its rich forests and mineral

deposits, became a direct holding of the shogunate, the military government. From that time on, poor as they were, the people felt a sense of pride in being residents of an area administered by the nation's ruler.

There were three peasant uprisings against local authorities in Hida from 1771 to 1789, known as the Meiwa, Anei and Temmei uprisings after the names of the eras in which they occurred. These were the result of harsh local administrative policies implemented by two government officials, intendant Ohara Hikoshiro Tsugumasa, and his son, district deputy Ohara Kamegoro Masazumi.[8] The three uprisings are also therefore known as the Ohara Uprisings.

Ohara Hikoshiro assumed his post as intendant of Hida in 1766. When he did, he moved forward two months the collection date for land taxes, which the locals paid in cash rather than the usual payment of rice.[9] In addition, in accord with the central government's general policy of conserving lumber resources, he announced a five-year suspension of logging in Hida. This threatened the villagers' very existence, since they depended on rice they received from the government in exchange for cut timber.

Land taxes at the time were based on a floating rate of exchange, whereby they were set according to the current market price of rice in surrounding areas. Ohara, however, increased the strain on the peasantry by ignoring the fluctuation in value that inevitably resulted from rich or poor rice harvests and attempting to instead establish a fixed rate.

INTENDANT OHARA Hikoshiro further demanded an extra three thousand *ryo*[10] from the peasants to use as a contribution to the government to facilitate its approval of his planned fixed tax rate. He also imposed forced labor as part of their tax burden. The anger of the farmers erupted.

In December 1771, a village assembly was called to discuss how to respond to the intendant's demands. At that time, a group of peasants began rioting and destroyed the homes of merchants who were in league with the intendant. In addition, around ninety village heads and peasant representatives from forty-six villages in Hida signed a covenant refusing to accept the new standard tax rate or to provide free labor.

They signed and affixed their seals to the document in a unique, circular fashion, with the names arranged vertically in a circle like the ribs of an open umbrella. In that way, no one could be accused of being the ringleader, and they could unite together on equal footing. This was a plan born of the farmers' wisdom.

After the uprising, when the farmers petitioned the intendant, he became furious and began persecuting them. One after another, those who participated in the uprising were arrested and subjected to the cruelest torture. In 1774, the government handed down a judgment concerning the uprising. One farmer was condemned to death, three were exiled and more than forty were heavily fined to compensate for the destruction they had wrought.

Furthermore, in 1773, before these punishments were decided, the central government decreed that a land survey would be conducted. Such surveys were enforced to determine the amount of annual land taxes. The last one to take place in Hida had been eighty years earlier, and the area had been designated as producing an annual yield of forty-four thousand *koku*.[11] The aim of conducting a new survey was to find an increased yield and thus raise taxes.

At first the intendant reported that only fields brought into cultivation since the last survey would be measured. But when the survey actually began, the surveyors were carefully remeasuring the old fields as well. From the farmers' point of view, they were barely making a living as it was, but with the increase in their annual taxes that would result from this heartless survey, even that would become impossible. The village heads and peasant representatives decided to petition the government to stop surveying the previously measured land.

THE FARMERS appealed to the intendant's office, stating that it was unfair for the intendant to break his promise and include the previously assessed land in the new survey. The intendant, however, coolly replied that deception was the way of the world and refused to entertain their plea. Desperate for the survey to be conducted in the manner that was originally promised them, the farmers of Hida pledged together to make that happen.

People's movements are inevitably driven by anger toward the unscrupulous actions of the powerful.

Grasping at straws, the farmers began discussing any possible means of dealing with the situation. They employed various measures in an attempt to directly petition the central government, such as pleading their case with the survey commissioner who had come to oversee the project, but all to no avail. What's more, the intendant, learning of their activities, reported them to the military authorities. Subsequently, those involved in the effort to stop the survey were summoned to the office of the commissioners of finance[12] in Edo, the capital, where they were imprisoned and tortured for their group opposition.

At around this time, contradictions in the government's political and economic policies were being exposed and peasant uprisings were starting to break out all around the country. The government, therefore, strictly outlawed group opposition activities and began cracking down harshly on anyone involved in them. Direct appeals to the government were punished with severe penalties that included execution.

But the farmers of Hida continued to petition the government anyway. They secretly sent more than twenty village representatives from the area's three counties to the capital to personally make their case to government officials. Those who stayed behind promised to care for their families, sending the men off with the solemn pledge that no matter what happened, they would not let them die in vain.

The farmers who went to Edo waited quietly for the right opportunity to submit their petition. In July 1773, a farmer named Zenjuro and five others from Makigahora Village successfully handed their petition to Chief Senior Councilor Matsudaira Ukon-no-Shogen Takechika as his palanquin passed by in procession on the way to Edo Castle. They were arrested on the spot. Meanwhile, a group of farmers from Maebara Village, led by a man named Toemon, were arrested after delivering a petition to the mansion of Matsudaira Tadasato, a commissioner of finance and the lord of Tsushima Province.

In spite of the arrests, the Hida farmers felt a ray of hope in knowing that their petitions had finally reached the government.

AFTER HE LEARNED what had taken place in Edo, Intendant Ohara Hikoshiro called together all of the village heads, neighborhood groups' spokesmen and peasant representatives of the 283 villages of Hida's three counties. He then ordered them to affix their seals to a document stating that the men who had delivered the petitions in Edo did not represent the interests of the Hida villagers, and that they saw the new land surveys as a reasonable measure and had no complaints.

If all of the farmers opposed the land survey, the intendant would be held responsible for the trouble. Ohara's actions were no doubt driven by this selfish concern.

When the village officials considered the possible punishment that awaited them if they didn't sign the document, fear took over and many yielded to the intendant's demands. In their actions, these so-called leaders, out of a desire to protect themselves from harm, betrayed the people whose interests they were meant to be representing.

In all times and places, the conciliatory actions of cowardly, self-serving individuals bolsters the cause of evil.

Outraged by this betrayal, however, some of the village

leaders refused to sign it. One such person was a young man named Zenkuro from Hongo Village. "How can we do this when we promised the men we sent to Edo that we would not allow them to die in vain!" Righteous indignation coursed through his body and he stood up resolutely on the side of the people. A meeting was subsequently held in his village. The courage of this one youth and his impassioned call for justice galvanized the other villagers.

Then, in late September, farmers from a number of villages began to assemble in neighboring Miya Village, Ono County, where they held a large gathering. With Miya as their base of operations, they combined their efforts. At night, they lit bonfires throughout the area, the scarlet flames a symbol of the people's anger. The numbers that gathered ranged from several thousand to ten thousand. They called on their fellow villagers to solidly unite in their cause, knowing that unity was the people's sole weapon against authority.

The farmers did not resort to violence. Rather, they carried out an economic boycott, refusing to sell the townspeople of Takayama, who sided with the intendant, such daily necessities as rice, charcoal and vegetables. In addition, after much deliberation, they decided to send a party of three thousand farmers to the intendant to petition for an extension of the land tax payment and demand an end to the torture of those who had been arrested.

MOST LIKELY intimidated by the sheer number of farmers that converged on his offices, and wanting to avoid a direct confrontation, Intendant Ohara responded positively to their petition. In their simple honesty, the farmers were too gullible. Thinking their requests had been granted, they were overjoyed and expressed their deep gratitude.

But in actuality, Ohara sent a request for troops from neighboring feudal clans in order to put an end to the farmers' movement once and for all.

It is crucial not to be deceived by those of ill intent. To be so good-natured that one cannot see through the schemes of such people is to bring about the tragic defeat of truth and justice.

In mid-November, several hundred armor-clad warriors launched a surprise raid on the farmers gathered in Miya Village. Believing that government officials would not dare attack them at a holy place, the farmers had conducted their meetings on the grounds of the village's Minashi Shrine, but this did not deter the soldiers in the slightest. The unarmed farmers fled for their lives, only to be struck down by bullets, lances and swords. The shrine precincts, awash with blood, turned into a scene from hell.

Many were killed and wounded, and several hundred were arrested—among them the youthful leader Zenkuro. This was later known as the Anei Uprising, after the name of the era in which it occurred. So many arrests were made that new prisons had to be built for their incarceration. The interrogations were extremely harsh, and even worse torture than before was employed.

About one month after the crackdown, on December 18, the villagers who had presented the petitions to government officials in Edo were executed. Their decapitated heads were packed in salt for preservation and sent to Takayama in Hida on the 27th, just as the year was drawing to a close. The heads were put on public display at Kiryugawara, the local execution grounds.

The snow that had been falling for several days was heavier than usual that night as the villagers made their way to the execution grounds to pay their last respects to the deceased. When they saw the cruel remains of their comrades who had given their lives on their behalf, their hearts were filled with a mixture of sadness, anger and despair. Hot tears of outrage and grief spilled down their cold cheeks.

In February of the following year, 1774, the land surveys, which had been temporarily halted, were resumed. In the end, Hida was assessed at yielding slightly more than fifty-five thousand *koku,* an increase of about eleven thousand *koku* from the previous survey. The heavier annual land tax was certain to further encumber the farmers' already straitened living conditions.

The farmers' desperate pleas had been completely ignored.

THE VILLAGERS who had been arrested in connection with the uprising were executed in December 1774. Four were crucified and nine were beheaded, with seven of their heads put on display for public viewing. Others were exiled to remote islands or banished from their homeland, and more than nine thousand were fined.

Zenkuro, the eighteen-year-old leader who courageously fought against the unjust actions of the intendant, was one who was sentenced to have his severed head displayed in public. He had a sixteen-year-old wife, whom he had hoped to return to alive, but that dream was dashed. He nevertheless remained perfectly composed. He had, after all, taken up the struggle prepared to give his life if necessary. That is why he feared nothing.

A person with mental preparedness is strong. It was no doubt Zenkuro's passionate resolve that had caused people to trust and admire him as a leader, young as he was.

One after another, the farmers were beheaded in front of the prison. Finally, it was Zenkuro's turn. When his name was called, he politely asked the official in charge if he might be allowed to have his last words recorded:

> *Beckoned*
> *by the breeze of impermanence,*
> *the closed petals*
> *of the red plum blossom*
> *now fall.*

> *I thought it was*
> *an evergreen*
> *but its leaves are falling.*

He then bowed to the official and signaled the executioner that he was ready. It is historically noted that Zenkuro's noble countenance in the face of death was praised by all.

Meanwhile, Intendant Ohara was promoted to the position of district deputy for increasing the tax yield of Hida through the new land survey. Those who had sided with him were also rewarded in various ways, including being given surnames and the privilege of wearing swords, both important marks of status in feudal society.

The authorities, who feared nothing but a united people, skillfully employed the carrot-and-stick approach in their dealings with them. Furthermore, seeking to end the peasant uprisings once and for all, they resorted to cruel and relentless persecution. But the flame of the Hida villagers' passion to fight such tyranny could not be extinguished. In the ashes of their pain and suffering, the embers of the spirit of resistance continued to glow.

In 1781, after the death of Ohara Hikoshiro, his son Ohara Kamegoro Masazumi became the district deputy. The following year saw the beginning of great crop failure that would ultimately result in a terrible famine known as the Temmei Famine (after the era name). Conditions were so severe that people had nothing to eat but the roots of weeds and the bark of trees.

ADDING TO THE SUFFERING caused by the famine, in March 1784 there was a great fire in Takayama that destroyed the homes of more than six thousand villagers. Despite these dire circumstances, District Deputy Ohara Kamegoro forced unreasonable demands on the people. For example, he declared that instead of reimbursing the farmers with the excess land taxes that were rightfully theirs, he was going to remit that money to the central government as an offering from the district.

For the third time the people arose. In 1788, representatives of the farmers went to Edo to report the injustices perpetrated by the district deputy. They hung petitions on walls around the residence of the new senior councilor, Matsudaira Sadanobu,[13] thus successfully making a direct appeal to the government.

The farmers could also state their case to central government officials who came to Hida on regular inspection tours. In Edo, they also made other direct appeals, using such strategies as submitting their petitions to Matsudaira Sadanobu as he rode by in his palanquin. With these efforts, the villagers' desperate pleas finally moved the government to action.

District Deputy Ohara Kamegoro was summoned to Edo for questioning. After a careful investigation, the government handed down a decision in December 1789. Ohara Kamegoro was exiled to remote Hachijo Island for inflicting injustice and suffering on the people. Officials who had worked with him were also severely punished, two of whom were condemned to death, while others were exiled or banished.

On the side of the petitioners, one of the farmers was also sentenced to death, but all in all the peasants were given a light sentencing. This may partly have been due to changes that were taking place in the central government. These changes included the end of the infamous Tanuma period[14] and the subsequent implementation of major reforms initiated by Matsudaira Sadanobu that were aimed at cleaning up the government. Nevertheless, it was an unprecedented outcome, with the farmers having their claims almost completely upheld and receiving lenient treatment from the authorities.

At last, the people triumphed over the tyrannical rule of the Oharas.

The renowned Chinese writer Lu Xun declared: "Many reform movements recorded in history were marked by a series of attempts and failures and further attempts, carried out by successive generations."[15] Indeed, the Hida villagers' glorious triumph was an incredible feat realized after many sacrifices and deaths, and through their efforts to carry on the fighting spirit of those who came before them.

The victory of the people shines nowhere other than in the continued dauntless struggle to rise up again and again, no matter how many times they are beaten down.

EVEN IN MODERN times, the people living in the Hida region continued to suffer from poverty. It is a well-known fact that from the late nineteenth to early twentieth centuries, many young women from destitute families in Hida were forced to cross over the treacherous Nomugi Pass to work in the silk-reeling industry in the neighboring Suwa region. The conditions they toiled under were extremely harsh and they suffered many abuses.

It was only in 1934 that a railway line connecting Toyama and Gifu prefectures, and also running through Hida, was opened. The people who lived deep in the mountains of the region learned that in order to survive they had to band together and support each other. This way of thinking, however, led them to isolate themselves from the outside world and remain steeped in old customs.

The flame of the Mystic Law was first ignited in Hida in 1958. The first district established in the region was Takayama in 1960, followed by Hida Chapter in 1964. But because of the tendency of the residents to cling to local traditions and time-honored ways, spreading Nichiren Buddhism there was difficult.

People who decided to join the Soka Gakkai faced the prospect of being ostracized by their fellow villagers, having their public water supply cut off or being disowned by their parents. But the local members did not give up. Believing it was their mission to transform Hida's destiny and make it a land brimming with happiness, they refused to be discouraged no matter what hardships they encountered. They kept this thought constantly in mind as they advanced with courage and tenacity on the path of kosen-rufu in their community.

Then, in February 1967, six months before Shin'ichi Yamamoto was to visit Takayama, a long-cherished wish of the members came true with the establishment of a joint chapter in Hida.

Yoshizo Tsuchihata, the new joint chapter leader, was a pure-hearted forty-one-year-old man of slight build. Born into a farming family in Hida, his father had died when he was just ten months old and his mother worked very hard to raise him and his three siblings. As a child, he had observed his mother's tireless efforts and decided that he wanted to do something to lighten her load. Thus, from about the age of seven, he started to get up early in the morning to help her clear weeds. Unaccustomed to working in the fields, he frequently cut his hands with the sickle.

WHEN YOSHIZO Tsuchihata became eighteen, he enlisted in the military. His elder brother had joined the air force as a teenager and was killed in action during World War II. Tsuchihata volunteered out of a desire to avenge his brother's death, but the following year the war ended.

With that avenue closed, the young man found a job at a company that manufactured pine-root oil, which was used in making solvents, preservatives and automobile fuel. Business was bad, however, because the demand for this material was declining.

Having endured low wages for quite some time, Tsuchihata eventually decided to open a firewood production factory together with his friend. He later got married, and then started his own firewood business. He did well for the first several years, but with the introduction of other energy sources such as kerosene, propane and electricity, his company gradually suffered.

Believing that effort was the key to happiness, Tsuchihata exerted himself to the utmost in his business. He soon came to sense, however, that in the face of changing times his efforts were futile. He spent his days racing about trying to raise money, but started to think of himself as a rat dashing around a sinking ship. A lover of sake, he began drinking so much that he spent a major part of his earnings on it. This led to conflict between him and his wife.

One year, as spring came and the mountains of Hida were sprouting with fresh green, Tsuchihata felt nothing but the blistery winds of winter howling in his heart. A relative who was a Soka Gakkai member, unable to stand by and watch what was happening to the Tsuchihata family, visited the home to tell Yoshizo about Nichiren Buddhism.

From the time that Japan, which had been regarded as a "divine land," had lost the war, Tsuchihata considered religion to be dubious and fraudulent and refused to believe that there was any such thing as God or Buddha. Therefore, when his relative began to talk to him about faith, Tsuchihata shouted angrily: "I hate religion! Don't come here again!"

Undaunted, the relative continued to visit Tsuchihata and speak to him sincerely and patiently about transforming one's destiny and about Buddhist philosophy. His words were logical and reasonable; most importantly, they were filled with utter conviction. Tsuchihata's view of religion began to change. Indeed, sincerity and tenacity are what moves people's hearts.

YOSHIZO TSUCHIHATA and his wife, Yasuko, decided to join the Soka Gakkai in November 1958. They had been particularly impressed with the idea of human revolution that members had explained to them.

Before starting to practice, the couple's disputes were usually centered on Yoshizo's drinking. Yasuko just couldn't tolerate her husband squandering their meager earnings on alcohol. Yoshizo had been thinking about giving the habit up, but he found it too difficult. He always had a large bottle of liquor on hand.

Four days after taking faith, he took a drink from a bottle he had been drinking from the day before, only now the sake tasted strangely bitter. At first he wondered if he was ill, but in fact he was in great condition. From that day on, he found it increasingly difficult to drink at all, and in the end he stopped completely.

Yoshizo and his wife regarded his giving up drinking—which had seemed impossible before—as a benefit of taking faith. In addition, as they recited the sutra, chanted Nam-myoho-renge-kyo and participated in activities, they experienced great energy and joy welling up in their lives.

Yoshizo's business situation, however, did not show any improvement. He was eventually forced to close his firewood company and find work selling securities and life insurance, barely eking out an existence. Yasuko also took a job collecting insurance payments, but the couple still didn't earn enough to cover their children's school lunches. Their debts mounted.

Nevertheless, a firm belief in Nichiren's teachings and a sense of mission to carry out kosen-rufu had already formed in Yoshizo Tsuchihata's heart. Refusing to be defeated, he resolved to transform his financial karma through faith. He resolved not only to become happy himself but to make Hida a land of great good fortune as well. He thus threw himself into sharing Buddhism with others and encouraging his fellow members.

In 1961, Tsuchihata became a district leader, an event that coincided with a particularly difficult financial crisis. The phone line he had installed for the purpose of Soka Gakkai activities was often disconnected because he couldn't pay the bill. When members complained that they could never reach him, all Tsuchihata could do was smile and say, "I'm terribly sorry. Our phone is broken."

PEOPLE WHO WANTED to collect money from Tsuchihata would go to his home while he was holding Soka Gakkai discussion meetings, thinking that he would not try to escape or hide on such occasions. Tsuchihata would have to leave the room several times during a meeting to talk to his creditors and plead with them to give him a little more time.

His financial karma was proving a great challenge to transform, but he continued to exert himself industriously. He began hauling scrap metal using a truck someone had given him. The vehicle, however, was in terrible condition. The left door didn't close properly and could only be held shut with a rope tied to the parking brake.

Unable to produce much power, the truck just barely chugged along. One day when Tsuchihata was traveling on the Meishin Expressway, he was pulled over and ticketed—for driving too slowly. He was going twenty-two miles per hour in a zone where it was required by law to travel at least thirty-one miles per hour. But with his truck filled with scrap metal, twenty-two miles per hour was the best he could do.

Though he was driving a wreck, Tsuchihata traveled the mountain roads of Hida in high spirits. He was promoted to chapter leader and eventually joint chapter leader, and on August 15, 1967, he welcomed President Yamamoto to Hida. But he still could not overcome his financial difficulties and was trying various means to resolve the problem.

Shin'ichi Yamamoto was well aware of how much the people of Hida had struggled and suffered over a long period of time. He also knew how hard the local Soka

Gakkai members had worked amid adverse circumstances for the happiness of their fellow citizens. That is why he wanted to encourage them with all his strength. He wanted to ignite the torch of courage and hope in their hearts.

As his car headed for the Takayama Community Center, Shin'ichi chanted earnestly for the peace and prosperity of Hida, as if trying to permeate the surrounding green mountains with his prayers. He arrived at the center just after eleven o'clock in the morning to find it overflowing with members. When Shin'ichi appeared, everyone cheered. He said: "Thank you for all of your efforts. This is a very beautiful place. Let us bring the dawn of hope to Hida!"

SHIN'ICHI LED the local members in a solemn recitation of the sutra and chanting of Nam-myoho-renge-kyo. There was no air-conditioning, and although electric fans were going, the temperature in the packed room soared along with the members' excitement. Shin'ichi was perspiring all over.

After the morning prayers and brief remarks by the leaders accompanying him from Tokyo, Shin'ichi addressed the Hida members in a friendly fashion. "At last I have been able to realize my long-cherished wish of visiting Hida," he began. "I am so happy to meet all of you." The members cheered and applauded vigorously.

"Incidentally," he continued, "today is August 15, the anniversary of the day the dreadful Pacific War came to an end. Japan rose from its defeat in the war and has become a prosperous nation. Many things happen in a country's history, just as they do in an individual's life. Each of us encounters various hardships. That is life; that is the reality of living.

"Embracing faith in Nichiren Buddhism doesn't mean that one's suffering and problems disappear. The point is whether we can overcome adversity with confidence and composure, rather than be defeated by it. That is what determines victory or defeat, happiness or unhappiness in life.

"Our greatness and strength as a human being is unrelated to our social position or status. A true champion is one who, regardless of what trying circumstances he or she faces or how bad things become, continues to advance with courage and hope without giving up.

"Faith is the source of power that helps us to break through and transform our destiny, no matter how severe the hardships we meet or how fiercely the storms of karma blow. And that is what the Gohonzon is for. I hope that all of you will continue to embrace the Gohonzon as you face myriad obstacles, and staying close to the Soka Gakkai, carry out your practice throughout your lives.

"If you do, you will experience wonderful benefit. You will develop into a person that nothing can defeat and attain indestructible happiness."

Beads of perspiration shone on the faces of Shin'ichi and the participants. But the members forgot the heat entirely as they held on to Shin'ichi's every word, their eyes shining with seeking spirit.

SHIN'ICHI CONTINUED: "Nichiren Daishonin states: 'The stronger one's faith, the greater the protection of the gods' (WND, 614). The stronger your faith is, the more the protective forces of the universe will aid you. The Gohonzon is endowed with the immeasurable power of the Buddha and the Law. It is by carrying out our faith and practice in accord with Nichiren's teachings—in other words, it is through the power of faith and practice—that we can tap into that great benefit.

"But many people chant with the thought that their prayer is simply too big to be realized, doubting the power of the Gohonzon. Since they are chanting with a negative attitude, of course their wishes won't be realized. If someone says to you, 'I know it's useless to ask you, but will you give me a hand?' you're not going to bend over backwards to help them, are you?

"The secret to drawing forth the power of the Gohonzon is to chant with firm, pure-hearted determination and appreciation. Compared to the Gohonzon's enormous beneficial power, your wishes are small things indeed. I hope you will rouse ever-stronger faith and receive ever-greater benefits from your practice. The next time I visit, I would like all of you to be driving new cars and to gather wearing fine kimonos and fancy suits, saying, 'Look how happy we've become!'"

At that time, very few Hida members owned cars and many of them were struggling financially. Shin'ichi's words therefore seemed like a dream, but they also became a source of hope and inspiration.

In closing, Shin'ichi said: "There are many other members here today who could not fit into this room, so I'd like to ask that all of you trade places with them so that I can have a chance to talk to them as well. Is that all right with you?"

The members smiled and nodded in agreement. Shin'ichi had been thinking about the members waiting outside for some time.

"All right, then," he said, "I'm sorry to ask you to do this, but everybody please stand up quietly." Shin'ichi quickly assumed the role of an event staff.

WHEN THE MEMBERS inside had filed out, Shin'ichi stepped onto the veranda and invited the members outside to come in. Happy cheers erupted and soon the community center was filled with fresh smiling faces. Shin'ichi again led morning prayers with the members from Hida.

Sitting behind Shin'ichi was a young girl who chanted vigorously, her face flushed with joy. Her name was Keiko Maruyama and she was ten years old. She couldn't believe that she was there chanting with President Yamamoto.

Keiko's parents were active Soka Gakkai members and ever since she could remember, the sound of chanting Nam-myoho-renge-kyo had been in her life. She began to chant on her own to deal with the problem of being bullied at school. When she was a baby, a potted plant had fallen off a shelf and landed on her left hand, crushing her middle finger and leaving her hand slightly disabled. Because of this, she became a victim of bullying when she entered kindergarten.

The other children looked at her curiously and made thoughtless, cruel remarks. They also shunned her. Young Keiko came to hate her left hand. She gradually became withdrawn, and by the time she entered elementary school she had stopped raising her hand in class.

Her parents would encourage her, saying: "Those who discriminate against and pick on others actually have impoverished hearts. Chant Nam-myoho-renge-kyo with all your might. That will make you into a strong person who is not daunted by anything."

A young women's member in her area also repeatedly encouraged her: "President Yamamoto says that children of the Soka Gakkai are lion cubs. Lion cubs don't cry and feel sorry for themselves, no matter what happens. Keiko, please do your best and never give up!"

These words gave Keiko hope and she chanted in earnest. She felt courage stir in her heart and resolved that she would no longer give in to tears of self-pity. As she continued chanting, she gradually regained her cheerfulness and began to speak up in class.

EVENTUALLY, Keiko wasn't bothered by her dis-ability in the least. A young women's member often said to her: "President Yamamoto is traveling all around the world working for peace and the happiness of all humanity. He is my mentor in life."

These words made Keiko wish very much that she could meet the Soka Gakkai leader. When she asked the young women's member how she could do so, she was told: "The Gohonzon answers all our prayers, so if you chant Nam-myoho-renge-kyo with all your heart you are certain to meet him."

From that time on, Keiko chanted in earnest to meet President Yamamoto. Then, a few days prior to August 15, she heard from her parents who were local chapter leaders that President Yamamoto would be coming to Takayama on that date. She had chanted nearly 1.5 million times. She asked her parents if she could go to the meeting, too.

"No children are allowed at the meeting this time," her mother said. "Besides, we need you to stay home and look after your little sister."

On August 15, her parents went to the community center in the morning. As Keiko chanted at home, an irrepressible desire to meet President Yamamoto welled up in her being. Thinking that she would be happy if she could catch even a glimpse of him, she decided to go out and stand along the highway that led to the community center in the hope that she might see his car. She thus left the house.

After about thirty minutes, Keiko arrived at the highway. She started to walk along the shoulder, heading in the direction of the community center. At an open space along the way a large crowd of people were gathered. They seemed to be Soka Gakkai members. It was the assembly area for members going to the Takayama Community Center.

Recalling her promise to her mother, Keiko hid behind a tree so her parents wouldn't see her, but a young man who was part of the organizing staff found her. "Please get in line with the others," he said.

AFTER A SHORT WHILE, it was time for the waiting members to move to the community center. Keiko hesitated, feeling bad that she had defied her parents' instructions to stay at home and look after her younger sister. But once the group started moving, it didn't seem right for her to step out of line and go home, so she followed everyone else. The thought that she might run into her parents filled her with trepidation.

The members arrived at the community center and waited in the courtyard. Soon they were invited inside. Pushed forward by the crowd, Keiko found herself in the front row. President Yamamoto, whom she had prayed so hard to meet, was seated right in front of her. She couldn't believe that she was chanting directly behind him.

As she chanted, her heart brimmed with emotion, and she thought, "The Gohonzon is amazing! My prayer has really come true!"

After the prayers, Shin'ichi turned around to face the members. Seeing Keiko, who was sitting there stiffly upright, he said, "Come sit next to me!" But Keiko was so tense that she didn't even hear him. Katsu Kiyohara, seated next to Shin'ichi, beckoned to Keiko, and Keiko moved toward her.

"Not to me," Kiyohara remarked. "President Yamamoto has asked you to sit beside him."

Hearing this, the other members broke into warm laughter. Keiko finally made her way to Shin'ichi's side.

"What grade are you in?" he asked her.

"Fifth," Keiko replied.

"I see. Please take good care of your parents and study hard."

Believing that it was children who shoulder the future, he was compelled to speak to her. He wanted to present her with something as a remembrance, but he had not prepared any gifts. He therefore took some sweets that had been placed on the altar and handed them to Keiko, saying, "Here's a little gift."

Keiko's face flushed with joy and embarrassment and, forgetting even to say thank you, she returned to her seat.

IT WAS A BRIEF encounter, but Shin'ichi's encouragement kindled the flame of mission in Keiko Maruyama's life. Feeling President Yamamoto's expectations for her, she decided to do her very best and study hard. With this vow in her heart, she hurried home after the meeting.

Eleven years later, in July 1978, Keiko would receive encouragement from Shin'ichi once again, at a Chubu Region leaders meeting held at the Chubu Culture Center in Nagoya. At that time, Shin'ichi heard from a local leader that the little girl he had spoken to on his visit to Takayama so many years before was now a young women's headquarters leader in that area and was attending the meeting.

Shin'ichi was overjoyed to learn that the seed he had planted in Hida years ago was blooming splendidly. He immediately composed a poem and asked that a local leader present it to Keiko during the meeting. It read:

What a joy
to witness your beautiful dance
in the garden of kosen-rufu.

When Keiko's name was called and she walked up to the stage, Shin'ichi spoke to her warmly: "When I visited Takayama you were a fifth grader, weren't you? I remember you well. I'll continue to watch over you as long as I live."

Shin'ichi wholeheartedly wished for her growth and happiness. He wanted her to advance along the path of kosen-rufu throughout her life, never being defeated by weakness. He hoped that she would become a leader who worked diligently, humbly and sincerely for kosen-rufu, and who was trusted by everyone. Trust, after all, is the force that advances kosen-rufu in the community.

At the Takayama Community Center, Shin'ichi continued to share guidance and encouragement with the members, hoping to touch their lives. The room without air-conditioning was packed full with members, and even with all the windows open, it was as hot as a sauna. Shin'ichi was drenched in perspiration, and several times he felt a wave of dizziness come over him from the heat. However, summoning every last ounce of his strength, he said to the members: "I hope that you will build a magnificent garden of happiness in Hida, turning it into a wonderful community of human harmony. If all of you stand up with firm determination, you can absolutely do it. I promise you."

IN CLOSING, Shin'ichi Yamamoto said: "I will never forget you. I may not be able to visit Hida that often, but I am always praying for your good health and long life, as well as for the prosperity of your families and your community. I will continue praying for you. Take care!"

It was after two o'clock in the afternoon when Shin'ichi left the Takayama Community Center. The summer sun blazed in the sky and the heat was oppressive, but the Hida members felt as refreshed as if they had just stepped out of the shower. In the same way that a cool breeze invigorates body and mind, meeting with Shin'ichi stirred new vitality in the members' lives.

From about this time, Hida started to become a popular tourist destination and undergo dramatic changes. The local government actively put its energies into enhancing the tourist industry, and the same year that Shin'ichi visited Takayama a film aimed at promoting tourism in the city was produced.

The following year, 1968, the national government designated the Takayama area as a Chubu Region Urban Development Sector. The funds allocated by the government were used to build roads and other public works projects.

In addition, Takayama, with its many historical structures dating back to the Edo period, such as the old government building Takayama Jinya,[16] became a sightseeing spot where visitors could savor days gone by. The same was true for neighboring Shirakawa Village, known for its traditional Gassho-style farmhouses.[17] More than anything, however, it was Hida's stunning natural beauty that attracted people nationwide.

In 1966, the year before Shin'ichi visited Takayama, only one hundred ninety thousand tourists had traveled to the city. But in 1968, that number doubled to nearly three hundred eighty thousand. In 1974, it rose to approximately two million annual visitors, and to this day Takayama remains one of Japan's most popular domestic tourist destinations.

Behind this success shines the wisdom and dedication of many Soka Gakkai members who prayed for the prosperity of their community and made that goal their mission. One such person was a member of the women's division who started a private school to revive the traditional culture of Hida that had been handed down over the centuries. Numerous members also took leading roles in various trade and local community associations, making a conspicuous effort to contribute to the development of their hometown.

EVENTUALLY, impressive benefits started to bloom in the lives of the members residing amid the mountains and rivers of Hida. After a while, the freight business set up by joint chapter leader Yoshizo Tsuchihata flourished, and his financial security was finally assured. When he retired, his son took over the business, allowing him to continue working spiritedly for kosen-rufu in Hida.

Some members became successful managers of local inns. Others surmounted family problems or illness. Each member in the region built a life of wonderful happiness.

Community development and revitalization are important issues anywhere, but they can be a matter of survival in underpopulated villages and mountainous regions. If, however, people lose faith in their community and give up hope, there can be no prosperity.

Community revival is born of the love people feel toward their hometown; it is inspired by each person's awareness that he or she is a protagonist in that endeavor. In other words, the key to revitalizing a community is to revitalize the hearts of those who reside in it.

Nichiren Daishonin writes: "All of the mountains, valleys and fields where Nichiren and his disciples live and chant Nam-myoho-renge-kyo are the Land of Eternally Tranquil Light" (GZ, 781). Wherever we are actively carrying out our Buddhist practice is the Land of Eternally Tranquil Light where the Buddha dwells.

That is why Soka Gakkai members, instead of searching for an ideal realm or happiness somewhere apart from reality, have lived out their lives with the conviction that the place where they are is essentially a treasured land. They have made it their personal philosophy and mission in life to transform that place into an ideal realm where they can raise the banners of happiness and victory, no matter what difficulties or hardships they face.

Realizing the prosperity of a community or region begins with transforming the mind-sets of the people who live there and cultivating the earth of the human spirit. It is in such effort that a strong sense of community spirit is fostered, resulting in the growth of luxuriant trees of progress, the blossoming of beautiful flowers of wisdom and the development of a fertile plain of happiness. This is the purpose of the Soka movement.

In 2002, the Soka Gakkai's Twenty-first Century Training Center was established in Takayama City. The Takayama Culture Center was later built on the same site. These centers have become a great source of hope for the future growth and prosperity of Hida.

NOTES

1. Nagano Prefecture: A mountainous prefecture located in central Honshu, the largest of Japan's four main islands.

2. Edo period (1600–1868).

3. JMA Seismic Intensity Scale: From 1949–1996, the Japan Meteorological Agency measured seismic intensity using a scale with levels ranging from zero to seven. From 1996, the scale was modified to include ten levels in total.

4. Johann Wolfgang von Goethe, *Faust: A Tragedy,* translated by Walter Arndt (New York: W. W. Norton & Company, 1976), p. 14.

5. Toson Shimazaki (1872–1943): Born in Nagano Prefecture, he was a poet, a novelist and the most well-known Japanese proponent of naturalism.

6. Yubari Coal Miners Union Incident (1957): A case of blatant religious discrimination, in which miners in Yubari, Hokkaido, were threatened with losing their jobs because of their membership in the Soka Gakkai.

7. Genroku era (1688–1704) of the feudal Edo period.

8. An intendant was a low-ranking local administrator of relatively small parcels of government lands during the feudal period, constituting in many senses the local government. A district deputy was a step above, governing a larger holding for the central military government, including collecting taxes, overseeing census registration and enforcing law and order.

9. As the principal staple crop of Japan, rice could only be grown on flatlands with sufficient water irrigation. Together with barley, it was traditionally used as a form of land tax collected from the peasantry by the proprietors of estates.

10. *Ryo:* A unit of currency adopted in the late sixteenth century.

11. *Koku:* A measure of rice used to set taxes and the salaries of government officials, among other things. One *koku* equals approximately 180 liters or five US bushels of unpolished rice.

12. Commissioners of finance: The duties of this position included supervising police and judicial matters, promoting agriculture, protecting natural resources, guiding the people morally and collecting taxes.

13. Matsudaira Sadanobu (1759–1829): A senior councilor of the Tokugawa shogunate best known as the initiator of governmental reforms implemented during the period between 1787–93.

14. Tanuma period (1767–86): Period during which Tanuma Okitsugu, an official of the Tokugawa shogunate, exerted his greatest influence on the policy of the central government.

15. Translated from Japanese. Lu Xun, *Rojin Bunshu* (Collected Writings of Lu Xun), translated by Yoshimi Takeuchi (Tokyo: Chikuma Shobo, 1976), p. 348.

16. Takayama Jinya: Once used as the office of the local government under the Tokugawa shogunate, it is the only remaining building of its kind today.

17. Gassho-style farmhouses, built between the seventeenth and twentieth centuries, are much larger than the farmhouses in other regions of Japan. Inside, they are typically divided into three or four levels, each of which was used as a workspace. *Gassho* means to join one's hands in prayer, a gesture that the steeply sloped gable roofs of these traditional houses are said to resemble.

Dance of Life

HOPE PLAYS a melody of joy in people's hearts. Where there is hope, there is vigorous advancement.

A wall of white marble designed in a grid pattern rose into the sky, glistening brilliantly in the sunlight. It was September 1, 1967, the day of the eagerly awaited opening and Gohonzon-enshrinement ceremony in the newly completed Soka Culture Center, adjacent to the Soka Gakkai Headquarters in Shinano-machi, Tokyo.

The seven-story structure had a three-story ell attached and a basement level, and its north and south faces were finished in white Yugoslavian marble, creating the appearance of a shining palace. The building's fifth floor was occupied by a large Japanese-style hall with *tatami*-mat flooring. There was another similar hall for large meetings in the basement, and the third and fourth floors together comprised a theater with tiered seating, where films, plays and concerts could be held. The center also had various conference rooms, as well as a library with all the latest electronic equipment, including automated shelving. Having utilized a new type of architectural design that didn't require large supporting pillars, every floor of the building was bright and open.

The construction of the Soka Culture Center was announced at the headquarters general meeting held on May 3, 1964. The groundbreaking ceremony had taken place in January 1966, and now at last the building was completed.

Awed by the structure's modern architecture and facilities, the members participating in the opening and enshrinement ceremony solemnly made their way inside. The fifth-floor hall where the ceremony was being held had a floor space of more than forty-five hundred square feet. With wood paneling made from six-hundred-year-old cedar trees, the space exuded dignity and warmth.

Participants also gathered in the meeting room in the basement of the culture center as well as in the third-floor meeting room in the adjacent Soka Gakkai Headquarters, where they could view the events through the latest closed-circuit television technology.

The new center was a magnificent building with cutting-edge equipment and facilities. Shin'ichi Yamamoto wanted to offer the best of everything to the youth, who would be active on the front lines of their respective fields in the future.

The ceremony began amid high spirits at half past ten in the morning. After a vigorous recitation of the sutra and chanting Nam-myoho-renge-kyo, greetings were delivered by various people, including a representative of the construction company in charge of the building project, the Soka Gakkai arts division leader, the culture department leader and others. Each speaker voiced their delight at the birth of this new citadel of Soka culture.

SHIN'ICHI YAMAMOTO was the last to speak. After expressing his gratitude to the center's architect, contractor and construction workers, he said in a powerful voice: "I am filled with joy to be taking this bold new first step in the creation of a third civilization together with all of you, my dear fellow leaders, from this grand Soka Culture Center." Enthusiastic applause echoed throughout the hall.

"Kosen-rufu is essentially the creation of a society brimming with a rich and brilliant culture based on the supreme philosophy and ideals of Nichiren Daishonin. It is the creation of a great civilization dedicated to peace and the happiness of all people. In other words, it is the flowering of a civilization that upholds the teaching of the Middle Way, the wonderful life philosophy of the indivisibility of material and spiritual.

"Today, both capitalism and socialism have become deadlocked, and there can be no mistaking that day by day, year by year, the tide of history—in Japan, in Asia and throughout the entire world—is moving toward the philosophy of the Middle Way. I wish to declare that this is the trend of the times. With ever-stronger conviction in this reality, let us once again set off joyously into the future, working together in unity and with great energy and pride.

"Nichiren Daishonin opened the path of kosen-rufu for all living beings, a path fraught with many challenges. And the Soka Gakkai, the representative body of lay practitioners who have championed Nichiren Buddhism, has also walked this difficult road. But now, at last, the time for the actualization of this noble cause of kosen-rufu is ripe.

"I would like to close my remarks today by pledging together with all of you to embark anew with fresh commitment, giving our all to further extending the golden path of kosen-rufu."

The innovative idea to name the new building "Soka Culture Center" had also come from Shin'ichi. Culture is the highest expression of human nature. Creating a brilliant culture requires the cultivation of people's lives and spirit as well as the fostering of rich humanity. That is the purpose of religion.

Shin'ichi was convinced that from such a foundation the most splendid flowers of culture in the broadest sense would bloom—not only in the realms of art and literature but in education and politics as well.

A T ONE O'CLOCK in the afternoon, following the opening and Gohonzon-enshrinement ceremony, a performance commemorating the occasion was held. It was the first cultural event to take place in the second chapter of the kosen-rufu movement, kicking off the start of the creation of a third civilization.

The curtain opened with a performance by a solo koto (a Japanese harp) player illuminated by a spotlight. Next came a celebratory Japanese dance in three sections—"Snow," "Moon" and "Flower"—exquisitely performed by twenty-six members of the arts division.

The "Snow" section, an original composition that conveyed the ever-changing nature of our lives based on the Buddhist principle of the Ten Worlds, was particularly well received by the audience. It had been choreographed after much thought and planning by arts division members who sought to create something fresh that captured the essence of Buddhism. The dance was filled with the spirit of building a new culture. Adopting the customs and manners of the late Edo period, it depicted the dynamism of human life as it undergoes various transformations—from the sufferings of hell to the tranquil state of humanity and then to the joy of the world of heaven and beyond.

In a complete change of pace, the stage then opened up to performances of modern dance and Hawaiian music, followed by some choral groups. The young women's Fuji Chorus, which had won first place in the Tokyo Choral Competition, performed three numbers, including the popular "Sakura" or "Cherry Blossoms." The Fuji Boys Choir and the Hope Girls Choir next gave an energetic performance of eight songs, including "Kazaguruma" or "The Windmill." Their joyous singing brought vigorous applause from the audience.

The show concluded with a rousing performance by the Fuji Symphony Orchestra. The strains of Beethoven's *Fifth Symphony* reverberated throughout the hall, played with passion and spirit by artists dedicated to bringing the flower of culture to bloom.

Shin'ichi Yamamoto had loved Beethoven's Fifth from his youth. Beethoven, who had lost his hearing and was beset by one hardship after another, stood up courageously and faced the relentless onslaughts of his destiny. Shin'ichi always felt as if this piece was a paean to the spirit of one of the world's great musical geniuses.

Thinking how the members of the Soka Gakkai, ordinary men and women, had transformed their destiny into their mission and triumphed, and how they were now striving to rise up and create a new civilization, Shin'ichi's heart surged with joy.

THE OPENING of the Soka Culture Center in Shinano-machi, Tokyo, was followed by the completion of the Kansai Culture Center in Tennoji Ward, Osaka. On September 10, Shin'ichi attended that building's opening and Gohonzon-enshrinement ceremony. From that time on, culture centers would be built throughout Japan and, eventually, across the globe. These would serve as symbols of the Soka Gakkai, an organization dedicated to promoting peace and culture worldwide based on the teachings of Nichiren Daishonin's Buddhism.

After the ceremony at the Kansai Culture Center, Shin'ichi traveled to the Shikoku and Kyushu regions to encourage members there. At the Shikoku leaders meeting held on September 11 in Takamatsu, Kagawa Prefecture, he announced a new motto for the region: "Be Reformers Building a Land of Happiness." That year, to mark the start of the second chapter of the kosen-rufu movement, Shin'ichi had traveled around the country presenting mottos to each region to inspire the members in their activities.

Kansai had already been dubbed "Ever-Victorious Kansai" in January 1964, and in June 1967, Shin'ichi had reconfirmed this as the region's motto. Kyushu had been given "Kyushu—Ever-Blazing the Trail" at a leaders meeting on July 9, Chubu received "Be a Stronghold of Kosen-rufu" at a leaders meeting on July 10, and Tohoku had been bestowed "Be a Citadel of Capable People" at a leaders meeting on the 15th.

In August, Shin'ichi had given Hokkaido the motto of "Be Pioneers of the New Age" at a leaders meeting held there on the 21st, and on the 26th he had presented Chugoku with "Creating a New Tide of Kosen-rufu" at a meeting for leaders in that region.

On October 18, after the September 11 Shikoku meeting, Shin'ichi offered the motto "Be a Model for the Nation" to Tokyo and the surrounding prefectures. Thus, every Soka Gakkai region in Japan had received its own motto.

In advancing a movement, it is important for the people involved to have not only a concrete goal but also a motto or byword that captures and epitomizes their aim and determination. By consistently reminding each other of that motto, they can stay true to their original purpose and make a fresh departure with renewed spirit. Mottos can also provide a sense of mission and pride.

The mottos that Shin'ichi gave to the various regions of Japan would go on to become the spirit and proud tradition of each area.

OCTOBER 15, 1967, was a beautiful day. The rainy skies of the day before had cleared completely for the Soka Gakkai's historic Tokyo Culture Festival, held at the Tokyo National Stadium. It was to be a festival of unprecedented scale, a great drama, an unfolding panorama of joy, a symbol of hope for the future. A total of sixty-two thousand members were performing, including forty-two thousand card stunt participants, making it the largest culture festival in Soka Gakkai history.

The total number of participants in the Kansai Culture Festival, which took place in autumn of the previous year at the Koshien Baseball Stadium in the pouring rain, was forty-one thousand, of which twenty-two thousand were involved in the card stunt. And the second Soka Gakkai Culture Festival, held at the national stadium three years earlier, in 1964, had forty-five thousand participants, of which thirty thousand comprised the card stunt. The present festival was clearly an unparalleled event that surpassed all the others in its scale.

The 1967 New Year's Day edition of the *Seikyo Shimbun* had carried an article about a discussion meeting that President Yamamoto had attended, at which he had been quoted as saying: "Let's hold a giant culture festival in

Tokyo in October. Culture festivals demonstrate how committed the Soka Gakkai is to the development of culture and to the creation of a culture of peace. So let's invite as many guests as possible to witness this. People who've seen our culture festivals in the past have gained a deeper understanding of our movement. These events speak for themselves."

The festival thus became a source of inspiration for the members in the greater Tokyo metropolitan area, and they worked toward it with keen anticipation. Meanwhile, the leaders of the young men's and young women's divisions resolved together to make it the best culture festival to date. Then, at the May 3 Headquarters General Meeting, the start of the second chapter of the kosen-rufu movement was announced. With that, the youth division leaders solidified their determination to make the upcoming culture festival, which would mark the beginning of this new phase, a tremendous success through their own efforts.

The festival took on added significance as a preliminary celebration in honor of the construction of the Grand Main Temple, which would officially be announced in a ceremony slated for October 12. This new edifice would serve as the fundamental place of practice for world peace.

PREPARATIONS for the Tokyo Culture Festival began in earnest from late June. A Festival Steering Committee was established with General Director Hiroshi Izumida as chairperson, and a preparatory committee comprised of youth members was set up as well. Vice

Young Men's Leader Naohiro Kubota was put in charge of overseeing all of the performances.

Kubota was a staff member of the Min-On Concert Association. Having been responsible for arranging Min-On–sponsored Japan tours by the Soviet National Academy Novosibirsk Ballet and Belgium's Twentieth Century Ballet of the Monnaie Royal Theater, he had become familiar with theater staging. His experiences in that area led him to conceive of the culture festival as one integrated performance with a common theme running throughout. This had never been attempted in a Soka Gakkai culture festival before.

One idea he came up with was incorporating the Seven Bells—the seven seven-year periods marking major advances in the Soka Gakkai since its establishment in 1930—into the central theme. He particularly wanted to demonstrate the flow of kosen-rufu from the period of the Fifth Bell. This was a period that had seen Shin'ichi Yamamoto rising up as a disciple after President Toda's death, becoming the third president and initiating a dynamic wave of advancement. Kubota also wished to depict the joyous activities of Soka Gakkai members toward the completion of the Grand Main Temple, which would coincide with the end of the Sixth Bell in 1972.

He further envisaged portraying the future image of Tokyo as a city of skyscrapers rising from the midst of green forests and fountains, which President Yamamoto had shared at the special Headquarters leaders meeting in March. He also wished to include the vision of the hope-filled future exemplified by the opening of the Soka Junior High School and Soka High School the following year.

The only theme that could embrace all of these ideas, he decided, was world peace. With that year marking the tenth anniversary of President Toda's Declaration for the Abolition of Nuclear Weapons, as well as the beginning of the second chapter of kosen-rufu, he was keenly aware that the time had come for the Soka Gakkai to decisively stand up for peace. His conception was also inspired by the fact that the Grand Main Temple would be the spiritual center where members, who were eagerly awaiting its completion, would go to offer prayers for peace.

The problem was how to combine all of these diverse ideas into a single, unified production.

NAOHIRO KUBOTA imagined the culture festival unfolding seamlessly to continuous music, as opposed to employing narration or whistle signals for scene transitions. This would allow the festival to proceed in one consistent flow. Kubota shared this idea at a meeting of youth leaders where the original plan for the festival was being considered before presenting it to the preparatory committee.

Many of the leaders liked his idea, but some also had doubts about how practical it was. If the entire festival was to proceed to the accompaniment of a continuous musical background, a single mistake at any point could throw off everything that followed and ruin the entire production. In addition, the festival was taking place in a stadium rather than a theater, and the acoustics weren't very good. There were concerns whether everyone could hear the music.

If Kubota's plan succeeded it would be a wonderful show, but there was a high risk of failure. Fresh challenges, however, are necessary in order to surpass previous accomplishments. In the end, the youth leaders decided to take on the challenge, fully aware of the difficulties in store, and they drew up their proposal for the culture festival based on Kubota's idea.

On June 24, the first Tokyo Culture Festival Preparatory Committee meeting was held. There, an outline for the festival close to the original plan put forward by the youth leaders was accepted and it was decided to solicit participants from the four divisions and begin preparations in earnest. Rehearsals for each program began in mid-July. Roughly three months remained before the big day. During that time, many individual human dramas unfolded as the various participants challenged themselves toward making the event a grand success.

On the day of the festival, a bright autumn sun shone down on the Tokyo National Stadium. Some seventy thousand spectators, including the card stunt participants, packed the bleachers, their excitement mounting as the one o'clock starting time drew near.

Approximately five thousand guests were also in attendance, including people from the worlds of business and finance, the media, academia, and ambassadors and diplomats of various nations. Many political figures were present as well, among them such cabinet members as the foreign minister and the minister of education, the governors of Tokyo and neighboring prefectures, and leaders of several minority political parties.

A GUN WAS SOUNDED, signaling the beginning of the Tokyo Culture Festival. At that moment, the section of the stands where the card stunt was taking place changed from all white to a curtain of horizontal stripes in thirteen vibrant hues of gold, silver, red, yellow, green and so on, fanning out from the center to the accompaniment of dramatic music.

Next, the cards turned to display Mount Fuji's majestic form. A gasp of delight rose from the audience. To the solemn tolling of a bell, the mountain's appearance gradually transformed, emerging from predawn darkness to the first hints of morning light and then growing brighter and brighter. The bell tolled five times in total, heralding the start of the fifth of the Seven Bells.

The audience was already captivated by the card stunt. Then, five thousand white pigeons were simultaneously released against the backdrop of Mount Fuji. They flew upwards, circling the sky above the national stadium and then disappearing into the heavens. Applause erupted from the stands.

The birds had performed magnificently, without a rehearsal. Assembling five thousand white homing pigeons had been no easy feat. The young men's members in charge of this event had scoured Tokyo and the rest of the Kanto region, and each time they found a place with a pigeon house, they negotiated with the owners for the use of the birds.

In late September, the *Seikyo Shimbun* reported on the young men's difficulty in finding enough pigeons. After reading the article, two brothers living in Iwate Prefecture who were members wrote a letter to the newspaper offering their two pigeons. *Even if they couldn't participate in the Tokyo Culture Festival themselves, it would be wonderful if their birds could*, they thought.

A young men's member in Fukuoka Prefecture also

sent some pigeons. In addition, the young men in charge of the event solicited the full support of various breeder associations. For their part, they studied how to care for the birds properly in order to ensure their health and safety.

Members took turns keeping a round-the-clock watch from the day before the festival when all the birds had been brought together. Now, the five thousand white homing pigeons soared into the sky bathed in brilliant sunlight, the sound of their flight echoing boundless hope.

The scene of Mount Fuji was then replaced with the words, "1967 Tokyo Culture Festival," which stretched across the stands in red and blue letters against a white background.

THE CARDS SHIFTED to display a single peony blossom in the center of the stands. Little by little, it expanded outward until a large peony filled the entire space. In the next instant, red and white plum blossoms appeared, and in the next, they became cherry buds, which burst into bloom. The image then transformed into successive displays of rape blossoms, violets, roses and then a brilliant flower garden with a fawn scampering through. It was like an enormous animated picture unfolding across the giant screen of the stands.

The card stunt at the Second Culture Festival in November three years earlier, in 1964, which also took place at the Tokyo National Stadium, had drawn great attention as a performance of unity. It was the first sophisticated spectacle of its kind to appear in a Soka Gakkai culture festival, in which participants used a variety of colored cards to exhibit a series of words and images one after another.

At the rain-soaked Kansai Culture Festival the previous year, the card stunt was further developed, making it possible to create moving animated images. This was picked up by the mass media and these card events came to be widely regarded as one of the special features of Soka Gakkai culture festivals. Resolved to create a new art form that was the ultimate expression of the beauty of unity, the leaders in charge of the 1967 Tokyo Culture Festival card stunt decided to fill the stands with 279 images, surpassing the fifty-two that had been presented in Kansai.

Thirty arts division members, who included Western and Japanese-style painters, graphic designers and illustrators, designed the pictures. As the performances that would take place on the stadium ground were decided, these artists became very busy drawing sketches. Their task was to create images that would serve as the backdrop to those performances, but often all they had to go on was a suggested theme, such as "The Joy of Youth" or "City of the Future." From there, they would develop a concept and then produce an actual design.

They spent long hours sharing opinions and ideas in the process of creation, talking through the night on many occasions. And even after they had come up with a complete design, it often ended up being rejected for one reason or another. Between three thousand and five thousand designs were made before the final 279 were decided upon.

SOME OF THE ARTS Division members working on the designs were well-known artists, including a painter who had won a special award in the Japan Fine Arts Exhibition and a founding member of a famous art association. But the selection process was so stringent that even the works of these artists were turned down. The members choosing the designs didn't know who had drawn what, and they would not accept any that failed to impress and convince every one of them.

But no matter how many times the work was rejected, not a single artist complained or threatened to quit. They had all completely put aside their personal fame and prestige. This was because they all decided from the start to work together to create the best card stunt possible and make the festival a historical event.

As a result, when one of their designs was rejected,

they sincerely reflected on its shortcomings and challenged themselves even harder. One young member of the arts division, surprised by their humility, remarked to one of the renowned painters: "I never imagined that a famous artist such as yourself would volunteer to design a card stunt."

Smiling, the artist replied: "I am a Soka Gakkai member before I am a painter. I am only doing what I can to contribute to our culture festival, which will open a new age of kosen-rufu. I understand that the festival will also be filmed, which means that millions of people will eventually see it. I think it's wonderful to be able to contribute to touching those people's hearts and giving them courage and hope.

"Our work also demonstrates how great Nichiren Buddhism is. This is a unique and precious opportunity indeed. In addition, it is rare for artists of different styles and ways of thinking to work together to create a new art form. I'm usually shut off in the world of my own creative vision, so this is a tremendous chance to receive new stimuli and inspiration.

"I'm hoping that through this endeavor I'll break through the shell of my small, narrow self and expand my state of life."

AS THE FESTIVAL drew near, the members engaged in the preparations for the card stunt became busier, with some even staying overnight at the workshop to continue drawing the designs. Then, from mid-August a new task befell them. The selected designs had to be transferred onto carefully measured seating charts, which were small-scale depictions of the stadium stands. Each seat was represented by a square on the chart and needed to be painted individually according to the designs.

Based on the actual proportions of the stands, each seating chart was a long, narrow band fourteen inches high and ten feet wide. To match these proportions, designs sometimes required extensive modification. There were forty-two thousand individual squares per chart, and painting one of these squares took about three seconds. In other words, to transfer one full design to a seating chart took one hundred twenty-six thousand seconds, or thirty-five hours.

Including several designs that were ultimately not used, a total of 450 seating charts were to be produced. Completing them in time for the festival would require a large mobilization of people. When an appeal was sent out to the arts division, some two hundred members offered their services. In addition to painters, the volunteers included actors, musicians and other types of artists. Though many of them had no experience with drawing or painting, they were eager to do anything they could to help.

One actress traveled to the workshop every day from the film studio in Ofuna, Kanagawa Prefecture, where she was shooting. Pianists, vocalists and even Japanese tea ceremony teachers participated as well, finding the time to do so in spite of their busy schedules. Some came during the day, while others came at night and worked until dawn. The workshop was busy twenty-four hours a day.

Once the seating charts were completed, numbered

color tables indicating which card to hold up at which point were made for each card stunt participant. Rehearsals then began, and the performers practiced switching their cards repeatedly on cue. Some of the animated moving pictures required that they change cards at half-second intervals.

AFTER DEPICTING a garden of flowers from around the world, the card stunt changed into an abstract painting whose main color was a fiery red. At that moment, two thousand young women's members in orange and yellow costumes entered the field and performed a dance titled "Joy."

This number started off a series of performances that collectively expressed the Soka Gakkai's vigorous advance toward peace that had taken place since Shin'ichi Yamamoto became its third president. "Joy" was a modern dance conveying the delight and excitement members felt at that new departure, which had come after a two-year vacancy of the presidency following the death of second Soka Gakkai president Josei Toda.

Hiroyuki and Keiko Ouchi, a married couple who were modern dancers, had choreographed the piece. They were among the twenty original members of the academic and arts division section no. 2—the predecessor of the arts division—that was founded in 1962.

Keiko's grandfather was Sadayuki Wainai. He is known for having succeeded in breeding sockeye salmon in Lake Towada—a feat that was previously regarded as impossible—on the border of Aomori and Akita prefectures in northern Japan. Keiko was born in Akita

Prefecture in 1921. She loved dance from childhood and went to Tokyo at the age of twelve to become a live-in apprentice of a famous modern dance artist. Though blind, her mentor was a leading expert in the field.

Keiko's life as an apprentice was extremely demanding. Required to serve meals among other chores, she was scolded harshly if she set the table with a dish or a chopstick even slightly out of place. She also had to polish the furniture for thirty minutes every morning. Each day was filled with stress and tension.

Working from early morning to late at night, she practiced her dancing in whatever moments she could find between chores. Only in the middle of the night could she practice to her heart's content, and she cut down on sleep to do so.

While her teacher had several live-in apprentices, none of them could endure this strict regimen and they all quit. But he had been carefully observing them. After several years, Keiko was given the opportunity to perform opposite him on stage. It was a difficult piece, demanding precision, endurance and a finely honed aesthetic sensibility.

Keiko's performance was superb. Through her rigorous apprenticeship, she had unconsciously forged her skill.

KEIKO EVENTUALLY married a fellow dancer named Hiroyuki Ouchi, who studied under the same teacher, and together they opened their own modern dance institute. Their new life began well. Their piece "Yamato,"[1] which they performed in a modern dance competition at an arts festival in 1941, won first prize and they were presented with the Minister of Education Award.

Soon after that, however, Hiroyuki was drafted to fight in World War II. Keiko was left to dodge the air attacks with their infant child in her arms. The war robbed them of their great purpose in life, dancing.

Hiroyuki and Keiko's first postwar recital was held in 1951. Their performance was highly praised by the mass media and they received wide recognition. The government of Ceylon (modern Sri Lanka) invited them to perform there, and once again they began to walk the path of artistic success and acclaim.

Despite their success, however, they had accumulated a large debt in borrowing money for their recitals. In addition, Keiko was also beginning to experience another major problem. She was overcome with anxiety about her future as a dancer, worried about what would happen when she lost her youth, and possibly her creativity, as she entered her fifties and sixties.

It was around this point that a neighbor told the Ouchis about Nichiren Buddhism. When Hiroyuki heard what they had to say about the Soka Gakkai, he was strongly opposed to it. As someone who had worked long and hard to achieve his position in the dance world, he believed that religious faith was for the weak-minded.

But he was having difficulty repaying his debts, and the stress of that situation had brought on a stomach ulcer. An acquaintance who was a Soka Gakkai member came next to talk to him about Buddhism. When he urged the couple to take faith, Keiko retorted: "So you're saying that if I take faith, any prayer I have will be granted, right? If that's the case, let me ask you this: Can I continue as a dancer even when I'm old? As I age, I will lose strength and my physical capacity will decline. Can you guarantee that I will be able to continue creating great art as long as I live?"

KEIKO OUCHI was certain that the Soka Gakkai member would be stumped by her question, but his confident response came instantly: "Of course you will. You will be able to keep working into your seventies and eighties, and your art will only improve as you get older." He went on to quote passages from Nichiren's writings and explained that Buddhism has the power to release our limitless potential.

Keiko was impressed by his resolute words and she decided to join the Soka Gakkai that very day. Her husband, Hiroyuki, desperately wanting to cure his ulcer, decided to do so as well. This was in July 1954.

Keiko and Hiroyuki both quickly experienced the first benefits of their new faith. Soon after they began practicing, they could schedule a series of performances, which allowed them to repay their debts within a month. And before long, Hiroyuki's ulcer healed. Overjoyed by this turn of events, the Ouchis set about introducing Buddhism to as many people as possible. The more they chanted for their friends' happiness and involved themselves in Soka Gakkai activities, the more they felt incredible joy rising from the depths of their beings and the passion and dynamism of life itself. It was a state of fulfillment that they had never known before.

Keiko was overcome by the feeling that the life force of the entire universe was welling forth inside her. As she experienced this power of Buddhism, she sensed that such life force was the very source of artistic creativity, and that as long as she had it, she could continue being creative at any age.

But it was a time of harsh prejudice against the Soka Gakkai, and the Ouchis met with strong opposition from other dancers. Many began giving them the cold shoulder. One dancer referred to them scornfully as "those Soka Gakkai dance teachers." Their original one hundred students started quitting six or a dozen at a time until their number dwindled to only a handful. The Ouchis livelihood itself became threatened.

But this only strengthened their faith, because they realized that they were experiencing what Nichiren was referring to when he wrote: "If you propagate it [this teaching], devils will arise without fail. If they did not, there would be no way of knowing that this is the correct teaching" (WND, 501).

ONE DANCE ARTIST remarked in disgust to Keiko Ouchi: "People say that the Soka Gakkai is a violent religion and that its membership is made up of the poor and the sick. How could you join a religion like that?"

Keiko replied with dignity: "To call the Soka Gakkai violent is completely baseless slander. Do you have any facts as to who did what to whom and where and when they did it? Many people make claims, but so far not a single one of them has provided any proof. These charges are nothing but malicious rumors concocted to harm the Soka Gakkai.

"As for it being an organization of the poor and the sick, I believe that the role of religion is to help those most in need. Many Soka Gakkai members have had wonderful experiences of overcoming financial and health problems through faith. Why don't you attend a meeting and judge the reality of the organization for yourself?"

The Ouchis often spoke to each other about how to deal with such situations. On one occasion, Keiko said: "Dear, it frustrates me to no end that I cannot get people to see the greatness of the Soka Gakkai's cause and what a wonderful organization it is."

"I know," Hiroyuki replied. "But I think that the best way to demonstrate it is for us to become outstanding in our art."

"I agree," his wife said. "We have to come up with a performance that people will watch and say, 'Now that could only have been created by a Soka Gakkai member.' But still, I find it ridiculous the way people blindly accept unfounded rumors about the Soka Gakkai and look down on the organization because many of its members are poor."

"Indeed. They may be artists, but in the end many of them judge others by such things as their social status, titles and personal wealth," Hiroyuki noted.

"That's so true. They think of themselves as special and look down on ordinary people. They think that being an artist makes them privileged," Keiko angrily said.

Smiling, Hiroyuki then remarked: "And weren't we just the same before we started practicing?"

THROUGH THEIR Soka Gakkai activities, Hiroyuki and Keiko Ouchi became keenly aware of the true brilliance and greatness of ordinary people. They observed the immense sincerity of their fellow members who, though struggling to feed their own families, devoted themselves to encouraging their friends and telling them about Buddhism, wanting to help them become happy. They witnessed their fellow members' lofty passion to build a new society while earnestly studying the Buddhist philosophy of life and seeking to understand the best way for human beings to live.

The Ouchis found that Soka Gakkai members, though they were all unheralded ordinary citizens, were the most noble and admirable people. As the couple continued practicing and their sense of mission for kosen-rufu deepened, their ideas about art also changed dramatically. They began to think about pursuing art for the sake of inspiring and empowering people, rather than for personal fame and recognition.

When they became members of the arts division, that feeling grew more powerful. But living a life dedicated to creating art for other people with no thought of money, authority or status put them in financial straits. It even became difficult for them to come up with the train fare they needed to attend Soka Gakkai activities. Nevertheless, they exerted themselves on the front lines of kosen-rufu, and on days when they weren't giving lessons, they opened up their dance studio for Soka Gakkai meetings.

Concerned about the couple's livelihood, Shin'ichi Yamamoto regularly offered them words of encouragement. On occasions when he would visit their home, he would encourage them wholeheartedly, saying: "I know it must be hard, but Buddhism teaches us that all of our suffering will become wonderful benefit in our lives. Faith is hope.

"You are pioneers in the realm of the arts. I hope you will not be defeated by anything and that you will bring brilliant flowers of Soka culture into bloom. Please carry out faith that flows like water. Your triumph will come ten or twenty years from now."

Nourished by such encouragement, the Ouchis worked energetically to promote kosen-rufu, and each time a Soka Gakkai culture festival was held, they took charge of the dance performances. For the 1967 Tokyo Culture Festival, they put their entire beings into choreographing the young women's dance number, determined to create art for the third civilization that would endure in people's hearts forever.

THE OUCHIS had received a request from the young women that the choreography to their dance number "Joy" incorporate refined individual movements into one splendid expression of the beauty of human cooperation. In addition, the music, an original, avant-garde piece, had already been composed. Given these parameters, the Ouchis faced an enormous challenge.

They were stumped. The stage was the field of the

Tokyo National Stadium and they were dealing with two thousand dancers. With such a large number of performers, it was most effective to use linear and fast-paced movements, but creating a sophisticated piece only with those kinds of moves was difficult. Their biggest hurdle in choreographing the piece, therefore, was how to elevate a mass performance to a level of great artistry.

On top of that, the participants were all amateurs. Many of them were stiff and couldn't lift their legs very high. Nevertheless, the Ouchis were determined to turn them all into excellent dancers who could proudly perform on any stage by the day of the culture festival.

Genuine victory comes from succeeding in challenging circumstances, and it is here that we savor true joy.

The members were all serious about doing their best. Day after day, they did stretching exercises and practiced basic dance steps, rehearsing with quiet diligence. Some went directly to practice after work, without even eating dinner. Others, wanting to save on train fare, would walk as far as they could in the direction of their home before purchasing a train ticket to take them the rest of the way.

In spite of these hardships, the members were all cheerful and brimming with hope. When they realized that they were taking part in a culture festival of unprecedented scale, all their struggles turned to joy. Over the course of the rehearsal period, a certain part of a song became popular among the participants:

> *As long as we keep sweating,*
> *We will never stop rehearsing . . .*

They had set these words to a popular song of the day, working out all the lyrics as they traveled to and from rehearsals. The song overflowed with the young women's fighting spirit, and as they sang it walking home in the dark together, the exhaustion of their efforts evaporated.

THE INITIAL choreography for "Joy" was completed at the beginning of September, but changes were made on a daily basis right up to the day of the culture festival in a ceaseless effort to improve the piece. Arts division members designed elegant yellow and orange Grecian-style dresses for the dancers. But when the young women rehearsed in the costumes, something wasn't right. Their black hair created a dark, heavy feeling, as opposed to the light, airiness they were trying to convey. Everyone therefore agreed to dye their hair brown and wear it pulled back from their foreheads.

One by one, they tackled the various problems that arose, but the piece was still far from complete and, of all the events of the culture festival, it was the most problematic. The formation changes required a high level of precision, but even the circles the dancers tried to form on the field were misshaped. In addition, somehow the "joy" of the dance's title wasn't coming through in their performance.

The day before the event, run-throughs of the entire festival program took place in the Tokyo National Stadium. The young women's dance, however, still hadn't quite come together. Yumie Fujiya, the head of the young women's division, was fraught with worry. "Joy" was the opening number of the culture festival. If it didn't go well, it could spoil the whole event. The leaders in charge of all the performances were also profoundly anxious. Keiko Ouchi, the choreographer, furrowed her brow and bit her lip. *We must do it perfectly in our last dress rehearsal today!* she thought. All of the dancers felt the same.

But the final run-through was canceled due to a heavy downpour. Everyone was shaken and overcome with dread. The young women's leaders encouraged the members with all their might: "Everyone, let's be positive! All the struggles we have experienced rehearsing under the hot sun during the day and on damp grass at night, all our sweat and exertion day after day, have been for tomorrow! We mustn't be defeated! Let's chant abundantly tonight and make tomorrow a great success!"

THE NEXT DAY the sky was clear and beautiful. Seeing this, the "Joy" dancers knew their performance would be a success. The anxiety that had clouded their hearts vanished.

The performance began. In their yellow and orange dresses, the young women created a giant "V" formation the size of the field. Their expressions were bright and cheerful and they exuded joy. Keiko Ouchi sat in the stands and watched their performance from the front, chanting fervently in her heart all the while. They hadn't had a single flawless rehearsal, yet here they were performing. Knowing very well how difficult it was to be on stage, Keiko was deeply concerned.

But all of their formation changes flowed smoothly, and the circular pattern, resembling a giant blossom, expanded beautifully in several layers of perfect rings. A portion of their number was an elegant dance set to the koto. At another point, the dancers ceased all movement and held completely still. Each formation was executed without error as the dancers glided gracefully across the field. The two thousand participants blended together to create a performance of unity, harmony and energy.

"Joy" ended amid the applause and excited cheers of the audience. It was a huge success. For the first time since they began rehearsing, the young women had performed.

Seated in the royal box, Shin'ichi leaned forward and applauded vigorously. Keiko Ouchi, holding back her tears, offered a silent prayer of gratitude. And Yumie Fujiya, the young women's leader, also in the stands, was ecstatic.

The young women's leaders in charge of the performance lavished praise on the dancers as they exited the field. "That was wonderful!" "You pulled through at the crucial moment!" Hearing these words, the young women were overcome with emotion. Soon their tears flowed freely, and they hugged each other as they wept with joy. They had not simply performed "Joy"; their very lives had become joy itself.

The incredible life-state of each dancer had broken through a wall of tremendous difficulty to create a highly moving performance.

THE CARD STUNT in the stands changed to a white background, on which a small red eagle emerged. The eagle began to fly with dignity across the white ground. Stopping in the middle, it spread its wings gradually until it filled the entire area. While this was happening, thousands of fit young men, bare-chested and wearing white sweatpants and caps, dashed onto the field, cheering vigorously as they ran. This was the young men's gymnastics event, "Fighting Spirit."

Their dynamic performance, incorporating various movements from such martial arts as karate, judo and aikido, unfolded powerfully to the tunes of Soka Gakkai favorites, "Song of the Sons of Japan" and "Song of Dawn." Perspiration glistened on the young men's sun-tanned torsos. Their muscular physiques testified to their fighting spirit.

In the three months of training and rehearsals for this event, they had all transformed themselves. At the outset, many of the members were weak or flabby and some were so uncoordinated that they couldn't even march in formation. Their practices began with an intense work-out. Day after day, they jogged, marched and did push-ups and stretching exercises.

They were all young men at the peak of their working lives. It was no easy thing for them to leave work and get to rehearsals on time. Some made special arrangements with their supervisors to attend rehearsals in the evening and then return to the office afterward and do whatever overtime was needed late into the night.

Those who did construction work and other physical labor were often so exhausted when they returned home from rehearsals that they collapsed as soon as they stepped in the front door. But they were all resolved to win, no matter what. They overflowed with fighting spirit to make their event a great success.

Determination, conviction and perseverance become

an incredible driving force that can break through any difficulty.

When the final run-through the day before the culture festival was canceled due to rain, the young men decided to carry on anyway. By rehearsing in such conditions, they hoped to engrave in their hearts the valiant spirit of the young men's division members to face the harshest challenges head-on.

THE PERFORMANCE of "Fighting Spirit," brimming with the power of youth, deeply impressed the audience. Observing the beauty of seamless unity conveyed through the young men's harmonizing of dynamic motion and stillness, the guests were moved by what they saw as an alliance of youth committed to building a new age.

At that time of rapid economic growth in Japan, many Tokyo residents were originally from the Japanese countryside. Young men in particular flocked to the exciting capital with its skyscrapers and expressways in search of employment. Many of them, however, came to the big city only to find that it was nothing like their dreams, and they ended up returning home.

The rivers that ran below the towering buildings reeked with pollution, and Tokyo's air was choked with the fumes of automobile exhaust. Prices were high and decent housing was scarce. Junior high and high school graduates who found work in the city did not lead easy lives. Most of what was available was in dangerous, punishing, low-wage construction jobs.

These young men tended to live in cramped apartments

with communal toilets and no bath. In addition, they traveled to work on packed trains. Many became lonely because of the lack of warm, nurturing human relationships in the metropolis. The city of glittering lights was also a city of sorrow.

Against this backdrop, the young men of the Soka Gakkai were burning with a sense of mission that they were the protagonists who would shoulder the future. With such determination, they were single-mindedly and vigorously advancing toward their individual personal goals. Filled with a strong desire to make a positive contribution to society and transform Tokyo into a second hometown they could be proud of, they strove to become the best workers in their respective places of employment and to extend a network of friendship and trust at their jobs and in their communities.

In the front row of the "Fighting Spirit" performance was a young man of particularly strong build. He looked gallant as he knelt in his pose with clenched fists and a determined expression. His name was Masatsugu Imaike, and he was a former sumo wrestler. He was one of the young men who had experienced bitter disappointment in Tokyo, but had risen up again.

After graduating from junior high school in Fukushima Prefecture, he went to the capital as part of a group recruitment by a metal foundry in Kawaguchi, Saitama Prefecture, just across the river from Tokyo.

MASATSUGU IMAIKE'S job at the foundry entailed hard physical labor that left him covered in dust and sweat. He burned himself numerous times pouring molten iron into molds. At that time, plastic was gradually replacing metal in many applications, and the future of the industry was far from bright.

Imaike's only pleasure was going to the movies and baseball games with his roommate, another youth from his hometown. But the following summer after they had moved to Tokyo, the roommate quit his job and returned to Fukushima. The thought of going on without his friend led Imaike to want to leave as well. So he took his summer vacation in Fukushima and simply never returned to his job in Tokyo. Forced to look for work in his hometown, he eventually found employment in a large chemical plant. There were three shifts, and the work itself was not demanding.

Imaike began to feel that he didn't want to spend the rest of his life working in a factory. He believed he had the potential to do something different, and what he really wanted to try was sumo wrestling.

Imaike was six feet tall and had a powerful physique from the time he was a boy. He had never lost in sumo when he engaged in bouts at school or with his friends. One day, he noticed a photograph of a famous retired sumo wrestler displayed on the wall of an inexpensive restaurant he frequented near his place of work. When he asked the restaurant owner about it, it turned out the man was a relative of the wrestler. Imaike then explained that it was his dream to become a sumo wrestler and asked for an introduction, to which the owner readily agreed.

Imaike went to Tokyo, met the former wrestler, and was introduced to the master of a sumo stable. The master invited him to start the next day. It was autumn of 1962, and Imaike was eighteen.

Life as a sumo wrestler was exacting, but having decided that this was the path he wanted to take in life, Imaike didn't complain. Not long after he joined the sumo stable, however, he injured his back while on a sumo tour. He was diagnosed with spondylitis, one of the vertebrae in his spinal column having disintegrated.

THE DOCTOR told Imaike that he'd be fine if he didn't overdo it. Indeed, when he rested he felt no discomfort; but when he trained, he experienced pain. Still, the only way to advance as a wrestler was to train harder than anyone else. Receiving injections of painkillers from the doctor, Imaike relentlessly pushed himself. He gradually became stronger and rose through the sumo ranks and, four years after entering the stable, he had reached the top rank in the fourth of the six divisions, *sandanme*.

The sumo world had great expectations for him, but as he approached his goal of achieving the highest ranking of *sekitori,* his back pain gradually intensified. His condition grew chronic, and the painkillers ceased having much effect. Unable to stand up straight, he could only walk stooped over. The pain persisted even when he lay down, keeping him awake at night.

During another medical examination, the doctor told him that if he continued overdoing it, the damage to his spine would be irreparable. The doctor's prognosis was in fact a declaration that Imaike would have to give up wrestling. Tears of frustration and anger filled his eyes as he thought of the dismal prospect of his life without sumo.

But the pain in his back told him he had no choice. He explained the situation to his stable master, saying that he would have to retire from sumo after the next tournament. The master tried to persuade him to stick with it a little while longer, but Imaike's body had reached its limit. He struggled fiercely against the pain in his final tournament and won a majority of his matches, giving his all to each face-off.

Imaike wrote a letter to his elder brother back in Fukushima telling him about what had happened and asking him to come to Tokyo and pay his respects to the stable master as a representative of the Imaike family. His brother did so, and this time the master accepted the young man's resignation.

After formally bidding the master farewell, Imaike went outside. He felt as if his life was over. All of his strength left his body. His brother, a Soka Gakkai member, followed him out and remarked: "Masatsugu, it's not over yet. Now it's time for you to win in the tournament of life. For that reason, I hope you will give Nichiren Buddhism a try."

SIX YEARS earlier, the entire Imaike family had started practicing Nichiren Buddhism back in Fukushima. They joined the Soka Gakkai immediately after Masatsugu Imaike had graduated from junior high school and gone to work in Tokyo. Imaike knew from their letters that his family had taken faith, but he had no interest in religion himself.

When he returned home after quitting the foundry in Tokyo, he was surprised to see how lively and bright his parents and the rest of his family had become. Until then, they had seemed to be merely dragging through their lives and all that came out of their mouths were laments, complaints and sighs. Now the entire house was filled with carefree laughter.

Looking in amazement at his parents' faces, Masatsugu commented, "You are all so cheerful." His brother replied: "That's because practicing Nichiren Buddhism has given us tremendous conviction that we can overcome any suffering through faith and absolutely become happy." From then on, Masatsugu developed a strong interest in the Soka Gakkai.

The Nihon University Auditorium, where many Soka Gakkai meetings were held, was near his sumo stable. Masatsugu was always struck by how energetic the young men directing pedestrian traffic outside the auditorium at those meetings appeared. That is why he agreed when his brother recommended that he give the practice a try.

But Masatsugu had somehow come to the conclusion that he would have to take a test to become a Soka Gakkai member, and this held him back. He remarked to his brother: "I would like to join, but I cannot read the sutras, so I don't think I'd pass the membership exam."

His brother laughed out loud. "Masatsugu," he said, "there's no entrance exam for the Soka Gakkai. You will learn to recite the sutra and chant Nam-myoho-renge-kyo as you go. The important thing is for you to firmly decide that once you've started practicing, you will carry it out to the very end, no matter how others may oppose your faith or ridicule you."

"So I guess that means I can join then!" Masatsugu exclaimed. This was a year before the Tokyo Culture Festival.

After retiring from sumo, Masatsugu stayed with a friend who was also a former sumo wrestler while working a part-time job in order to save enough money to rent his own apartment.

AFTER GIVING UP sumo, Masatsugu Imaike fell into a deep depression. Having lost his goal in life, he didn't feel motivated to do anything.

Eventually, he found an apartment in Tokyo's Shinjuku Ward. He enshrined his Gohonzon there and began learning the prayers with the local members and participating in Soka Gakkai activities. At one point, he mentioned his persistent back pain to a fellow young men's member, who said to him with complete confidence: "Don't worry! You can overcome every difficulty with faith and lead a truly wonderful and fulfilling life!"

Imaike wasn't fully convinced, but as he continued practicing, he began to notice his terrible pain subsiding. At first he thought it was because he had stopped the hard physical training of his sumo days. But when he thought of how common it was for sumo wrestlers to suffer from acute back pain even when they took time off to recuperate, he recognized this as a benefit of his Buddhist practice. This enabled him to deepen his faith, and he started to believe that his life was going to open up. At that moment, a ray of hope penetrated his heart that until then had been heavy with depression.

A short time later, Imaike heard about the planned Tokyo Culture Festival from a young men's leader, who said: "We're looking for participants for the group gymnastics event of the culture festival that will be held in October. This festival, in a sense, is an opportunity to show the world that the Soka Gakkai is an organization committed to peace and human happiness. It will be an event that will go down in the annals of kosen-rufu. Why don't you take part and create a wonderful memory of your youth?"

"I'd love to!" Imaike replied.

Imaike was determined to give his all to the culture festival. Rehearsals began in mid-July, and the participants were in high spirits. Imaike could feel their burning enthusiasm. He was particularly impressed by the members of the substitute squad. The original number of performers needed for this program had been reduced, and so those not kept on as regulars agreed to be substitutes. But they also practiced every day, just like the regulars, and joined in all the chanting sessions.

THERE WAS very little chance that the members of the substitute squad would actually perform, but none of them complained or grumbled about this. In fact, they went out of their way to watch over the performers' belongings and to keep the rehearsal area tidy to ensure that no one tripped or injured themselves during practice.

Masatsugu Imaike couldn't understand why these members were so dedicated, even though it was almost guaranteed that they wouldn't be performing. One day, he asked a member of the substitute team about it. "Of course I'd like to perform," the member said, "but our real purpose is to make the culture festival a tremendous success and to launch a new wave of kosen-rufu. We all signed up for the festival with the spirit to do anything necessary to make that happen. I think those participating as clean-up crew and traffic control staff must have the same commitment."

Imaike was struck by the selfless attitude of the substitute squad members, who had overcome their own personal desires and were united in their determination to ensure the culture festival's success as well as the advancement of kosen-rufu. Taking their duties as their mission, they felt great pride and joy in what they were doing. Moved by their spirit, Imaike thought to himself: *In contrast, I have always tended to be caught up in my own little world and my own concerns. That is probably why my life seemed over when my wrestling career came to an end and my dreams were shattered.*

Observing the other young men was very thought-provoking for Imaike. Rehearsals were filled with one touching experience after another. He saw members who were struggling with the moves stay late to practice on their own after everyone else had gone home, fighting back tears of frustration. Such members taught Imaike the spirit of challenging hardships.

Perhaps due to his large stature, Imaike himself was having difficulty keeping up with the others during rehearsals. Although the leader in charge frequently pointed this out to him, the sight of everyone working so hard kept him from becoming disheartened. In addition, the encouragement of the leaders and the other young men was a great source of support. "Do your best, and don't give up!" "We're sure to succeed if we work together!" In words like these, Imaike felt boundless human warmth. *I'm not alone*, he thought. *I have friends in faith.*

THROUGH THE UNITY of all its participants, the "Fighting Spirit" performance steadily improved and approached perfection. Little by little, the members began to feel confident that they would succeed. Masatsugu Imaike also sensed his own life changing dramatically as the days passed. The frustration and depression that weighed on him evaporated, and the future shone with hope.

Thinking that it would be impossible for them to express a true "fighting spirit" in their performance unless they made progress in their own efforts to spread Buddhism, the young men had vowed to each other that they would show personal results in that endeavor.

Imaike also strove to share Nichiren Daishonin's teachings with others. He told his friends of his first benefit in faith of overcoming his back pain and of the greatness of the Soka Gakkai that he experienced through rehearsing for the culture festival. "Buddhism imparts hope," he would say, "and I am convinced that faith helps us to open up a new life." This was his honest feeling as well as his firm determination.

Earnest words move people's hearts.

Hearing what Imaike had to say, three friends he knew either through sumo or his part-time job began practicing in quick succession. By the time of the culture festival, Imaike had strongly resolved to live out his life as a member of the Soka Gakkai. He had discovered the meaning and purpose of his life in the goal of kosen-rufu, which aims for the happiness of all people and the prosperity of society.

He was determined not to be defeated, to dedicate his life to kosen-rufu and to adorn his life with brilliant achievement. The culture festival had given Imaike a new lease on life.

In their "Fighting Spirit" performance on the day of the festival, the young men's members forcefully thrust their fists into the air as if to vanquish the negative forces of the universe. Their cry of "Yeah!" echoed into the clear autumn sky like an explosion of fighting spirit. As he performed, Imaike caught sight of Shin'ichi seated in the stands. In his heart he called out: "Sensei! I'm now in the most glorious arena of all!"

THE CARD STUNT in the stands changed from a red eagle with outstretched wings to a famous depiction of Mount Fuji by the eighteenth-century woodblock artist Katsushika Hokusai. Thus began a folk dance performance titled "The Japanese Tide" by forty-two hundred members of the women's division. They performed a variety of traditional dances to lively music, and their costumes—bright, vibrant combinations of either blue and white or red and white—emphasized their enthusiasm and high spirits.

Their faces shone with sun-like brilliance, exuding the joy, hope and energy that come from practicing Nichiren Buddhism.

Among the performers was a woman who had once suffered from various illnesses, including asthma and neuralgia, and had constantly been derided by others as a result. Another, having struggled with poverty and family discord, had even contemplated suicide more than once. But all of them had risen up from the depths of suffering through faith, resolutely challenged their destinies and exerted themselves wholeheartedly for kosen-rufu. In so doing, they overcame their personal weaknesses, transformed their family situations and achieved lives of great victory.

One such person who had faced the onslaughts of her destiny head-on was Takako Kubokawa. She looked impressive in her headband as she held her lance high while performing the "Takeda Bushi" folk dance. Tucked into a pocket sewn inside her kimono was a photograph of her late husband. He had been a building contractor who was known and respected as a master carpenter. In the photograph, he was at work on a roof, smiling with a hammer in hand.

As group leaders, Takako and her husband had achieved many victories in their kosen-rufu activities. Together they had traveled to such outlying regions as Fukushima and Nagano prefectures to enable their friends and families to embrace Buddhism, sometimes becoming deeply frustrated with the difficulty of the task.

For Takako, her husband was a comrade in their shared struggle and a partner with whom she had walked side by side along the path of kosen-rufu. But now he was gone. He passed away serenely on a snowy day in February of that year as a result of injuries sustained in an automobile accident. His countenance at death was that of someone peacefully sleeping. He left four children behind, the eldest a young man of eighteen.

WHEN TAKAKO KUBOKAWA lost her husband, she lost her main pillar of emotional support. But she lifted herself up from the depths of her grief by telling herself: *If I remain sad, he'll only be sad. Even with faith, life is full of difficulties and times of sadness. The point of this practice is not to be defeated by them. From now on, I will work for kosen-rufu for the both of us. And I'll raise our four children into fine adults and realize genuine happiness.*

Faith gives us the life force to overcome all sufferings and obstacles.

Fortunately, by renting out the house that her husband had left her, Takako and the children could provide modestly for themselves. When she heard that the women's division members would be performing folk dances at the Tokyo Culture Festival, she immediately volunteered. She regarded the festival as an opportunity to mark a fresh start in her life.

Her second eldest son also participated as a member of the card stunt.

As she danced during the festival, Takako wielded her lance with all her might, her motions filled with vigor and energy. *Are you watching?* she addressed her husband in her thoughts. *I'm all right now. As a mother dedicated to kosen-rufu, I will raise our children into fine successors who will carry on the Soka movement!* The field at the national stadium became, for Takako, the brilliant stage on which she made a pledge and a new beginning.

The sun shone down brightly on the field, as if smiling on the dancers. When the women's division performance ended, the card stunt changed to show a blue planet Earth and an airplane, which flew across the sky to the thundering sound of a jet engine. Then, out came the Brass Band and Fife and Drum Corps, whose performance was entitled "A Wave Across the World." Through such pieces as "Around the World in Eighty Days" and "La Cumparsita," they expressed how the wave of kosen-rufu was spreading across the globe. The spectators were captivated by the beautiful performance of the Fife and Drum Corps, a first-rate musical group of which the Soka Gakkai was proud.

A bell then sounded again and the card stunt changed to depict waves in the ocean undulating until the stands were filled with mighty breakers. A sailboat appeared in the distance, becoming larger as it drew closer, and a brilliant rainbow stretched over the sea.

THE BELL tolled six times. From this point, the culture festival featured performances representing Soka Gakkai events that would take place by the end of the sixth of the Seven Bells, by 1972. The opening program of this section was a gymnastics display by 1,540 high school division members entitled "The Strength of Youth." This was the first time for the high school division members of the Tokyo metropolitan area to participate in a culture festival. The members were filled with excitement as they began their performance.

They danced vibrantly across the field to such tunes as the "High School Division Song," their brisk movements evoking an image of young bamboo shoots reaching into the skies of the future. Finally, each performer took out a bolt of cloth and created a design in blue, yellow and red, framed by a white border across the field. The image was a fountain pen flanked on either side by stylized phoenix wings—the emblem of the Soka Junior High School and Soka High School, which were scheduled to open in Tokyo the following spring. The wing on the left was blue representing wisdom, the pen was yellow for glory and the wing on the right was red for passion. These were the schools' colors and mottoes. The cards in the stands simultaneously flashed the words *wisdom, glory* and *passion,* aligned with their respective colors on the field.

Vigorous applause erupted from the spectators.

Recreating the emblem on the field had proven to be one of the most difficult tasks of the entire festival. In particular, the curves of the wings on either side of the pen inevitably came out misshaped, ruining the emblem's symmetry. During rehearsals, the high school division members practiced this part of their performance dozens of times until they memorized their positions.

Some of the performers were night-school students. Since they worked during the day and went to school in the evening, the only time they could rehearse with everyone was on Sundays. They therefore made various efforts to practice on their own, such as getting together with other members studying at their schools to go over the routines after class.

At one night school, there were fifteen members taking part in the performance. These students gathered in a nearby park after school and had their fellow performers who were daytime students come and teach them the latest moves.

Because their time was limited, the night-school students practiced with great intensity. They burned with the youthful passion to challenge all hardships.

SHIN'ICHI CONTINUED to applaud the high school division members as they spiritedly exited the field. He immediately sent them a message: "Your depiction of the Soka schools' emblem was perfect. The audience was deeply impressed. You displayed the power of Soka youth who will shoulder the next generation. Thank you for all your efforts. Please take a rest now."

When the high school division members heard President

Yamamoto's message, they hugged each other and shared their joy and excitement at having triumphantly completed their program. "We did it!" "It was a success!" At that moment, all the struggles they went through with rehearsals and doing homework late at night were transformed into joy, pride and confidence, and became a wonderful memory of their youth.

The sweat of our efforts becomes the greatest treasure of our lives.

Next came a joint mass calisthenics performance titled "Construction" by the members of the young men's and young women's divisions. This event was to show the construction of an ideal city, based on the future vision of Tokyo as an international metropolis that Shin'ichi Yamamoto had articulated at the special Headquarters leaders meeting held in March of that year.

At that meeting, Shin'ichi, as a devoted citizen of his hometown Tokyo, had summed up in ten points his ideas for addressing the city's various problems—including the daily commuter rush, urban pollution and the housing shortage—and making it into a livable, people-focused metropolis. Among his proposals were the construction of high-rise apartment complexes that would ensure adequate housing for each resident; an elevated transportation network of monorails and expressways; green parks where people could rest and relax or engage in healthy exercise; cultural facilities for the promotion of the arts; and pleasant, pollution-free industrial zones.

Overall, Shin'ichi envisioned a "metropolitan Tokyo of skyscrapers rising among green forests and fountains." In the same speech, Shin'ichi had also emphasized the importance of fostering a love for Tokyo among its residents. Many people were only living in the city because of their jobs. As a result, they felt little attachment to their communities and there was no sense of solidarity or warmth among them. In fact, it was not rare for people to be unfamiliar with the faces and names of their next-door neighbors.

WHAT WOULD it take to transform Tokyo into an ideal city that its residents could be truly proud of? Of course, such governmental measures as building affordable housing and controlling pollution were indispensable, but perhaps the most important prerequisite was fostering residents' love for their community. As Nichiren states: "If the minds of living beings are impure, their land is also impure" (WND, 4). The key to the state of the environment in which people live is found in their minds or attitudes. It is also people who can move the government, and who can join together with shared goals and expand networks of friendship and unity. When citizens don't care about the place they live, and become self-centered and negative, their community will also decline.

Shin'ichi strongly felt that Soka Gakkai members had a social responsibility to cultivate in the hearts of their fellow citizens a love for the community and an awareness that they are the protagonists in the construction and revitalization of their community. Sharing Shin'ichi's spirit, the members of the young men's and young women's divisions strove to convey the image of Tokyo as an international city through their performance of "Construction" in the culture festival.

A Flower Brigade of eight hundred young women's members wearing red dresses and holding silver hoops performed a beautiful dance on the field. Next came the Ladder Brigade comprised of 1,440 young men clad in blue shirts and white sweatpants. Using more than two hundred thirteen-foot steel ladders, they formed a series of impressive geometric patterns that suggested a city of skyscrapers. One formation involved connecting two ladders vertically with a young man on top striking various poses. This part of the performance required a high level of technical skill, and the slightest misstep could have resulted in a serious accident.

The success of these ladder exercises depended upon the young men's ability to climb up and down the ladders with great speed. With this in mind, the participants focused on strengthening their legs and arms, doing squatting jumps and fist clenches. At home, they fortified their grips by squeezing a rubber ball and also by wringing their washcloths in the bath.

NO DOUBT DUE to their intensive training, the Ladder Brigade's performance came off without a hitch. The spectators loudly cheered their ladder towers that reached high into the sky. Next the Forest Brigade of fifteen hundred young women's members wearing green dresses and carrying vivid green pompoms came out and began their dance, portraying the image of a lush forest swaying in the breeze. The Flower Brigade then joined them and together they created multilayered rings of flowers and greenery. For the crescendo, a "ladder fountain" was constructed in the center of the rings. Several young men climbed to the top and, through body movements that included a handstand at the pinnacle, created an image with their blue-and-white-clad figures of water spouting from a fountain.

The youth members had created a city of peace, with flowers blooming around a lovely fountain in a verdant forest. The card stunt also showed a city scene of skyscrapers surrounded by trees, green lawns and colorful flower beds along with a giant fountain. The spectators gasped in awe and applauded vigorously, many of them sensing the young people's love for their community and their passion to transform Tokyo into an ideal international city through their performance.

The spirit of these youth was the hope of Tokyo, Japan's capital, and the driving force for the city's future construction.

People's attitudes, awareness and unity are what change a city, a community and a society.

The Tokyo Culture Festival was approaching its climax. The sound of fireworks echoed over the sound system as the card stunt in the stands displayed an image of fireworks celebrating the arrival of a new age. Some twenty-five hundred young men dressed in all white poured onto the field for another young men's mass gymnastics performance titled "A New Age."

The passion and power of youth creates a new age. Through their performance, these young men wished to convey their vow to build an age in which the people triumph, an age of respect for life, freedom and equality.

To the accompaniment of rousing music, a five-story human pyramid and a three-story human tower were erected and then brought down in an instant. Dozens of human windmills then went up and began turning in unison as human rockets were shot in the air, and a human bridge was constructed.

"A NEW AGE" unfolded in an impressive succession of displays. The audience cheered and exclaimed in amazement at each one.

"Be the best in the world!"—this had been the young men's byword as they rehearsed for the performance. At that time, the Czechoslovak Spartakiad was globally renowned as the greatest sports festivals of their kind. But they had been held under state patronage. If the Soka Gakkai culture festival, which was carried out entirely through the efforts of ordinary citizens, could be even more spectacular than the Spartakiads, it would demonstrate to the world the infinite potential of the people.

The young men's division members resolved to do just that. They watched films of various Spartakiads and studied them closely, striving to make each of their displays the best ever. The highlight of their performance was the five-story human tower. The finale of this event was a portrayal of the Grand Main Temple, which construction would soon begin. On the ground, the young men formed a pond in the shape of an eight-petal lotus blossom with a fountain resembling the one being built in the courtyard of the Grand Main Temple. A five-story human tower was raised in the middle to represent water jetting from the fountain.

Until that time, the highest human tower erected at a Soka Gakkai culture festival had been four stories, so this attempt at five was a first. The young men had in fact never heard of a tower of this height being successfully performed anywhere. When they consulted with gymnastics experts, they were told that though it might be achieved with the use of equipment, it would be extremely difficult to do without any aids. But this only fanned the members' enthusiasm. Inspired by the idea of a challenge, they became determined to set a new record.

Indeed, it is by directly taking on obstacles that the door to a new age is opened.

The young men did their research and decided that the bottom story should comprise twenty members in two concentric circles facing each other. The second story would have ten members, the third, six, the fourth, three and the fifth and top story, one. But when they actually tried to construct it, they found the task impossible.

No matter how many attempts they made, the tower collapsed.

They made weight calculations. They tested various shoulder and hand positions. They racked their brains to find a solution.

WHEN THEY ANALYZED the reason the five-story human tower kept collapsing, the young men determined it was because the members on the supporting layers did not have the strength in their lower backs to remain steady. They thus returned to the basics and started lower-body training, which included such exercises as walking in a squat position with someone on their shoulders. But they still couldn't get the five-story tower to stay standing, and some began to think that it was perhaps impossible. Then, one young man said, "Chant Nam-myoho-renge-kyo! Chanting Nam-myoho-renge-kyo is our only hope!" Everyone agreed, and they began holding intensive chanting sessions after practice.

Nine days before the culture festival, on October 6, they were desperately attempting the five-story tower, determined to succeed before the actual event. During the rehearsal, all the people began to chant spontaneously under their breath. They all concentrated intensely as the members on the top layers struggled to hang on even when their foot started slipping off the shoulder of the person below. Others managed to remain in place despite being accidentally kicked in the face by the person above. The tower rose story by story as the young men continued single-mindedly chanting until at last all five stories were standing.

They did it again during rehearsal the next day, under the worst of possible conditions. It was raining, making it harder to hold their footing, but the fact that they succeeded even in those adverse circumstances gave the members great confidence.

The more difficulties people overcome, the more they shine with self-confidence and pride.

The card stunt in the stands displayed a picture of the Grand Main Temple, while the young men on the field formed the eight-petal lotus pond. Then, to the accompaniment of the festival's rousing theme music, "Song of a New Age," the five-story human tower began to rise in the pond's center. One by one, the stories rose, until the fourth was in place. Only the fifth and final remained. The spectators watched on with bated breath. The solitary youth climbed onto the top and stood up with composure. Slowly, he stretched out his arms. It was the first five-story human tower to be achieved in the history of the Soka Gakkai's culture festivals.

A roar of excitement and thunderous applause shook the stands.

Down on the field, the young men restrained themselves from shouting out with joy, holding on tight as they continued to support each other in the tower.

THE APPLAUSE seemed to go on forever. The young men's members had dynamically shown the intangible power of faith through their accomplishment of the five-story human tower, a feat of incredible human strength. That tower, constructed through deep faith and bonds of friendship, represented a monumental achievement of their youth.

From that time on, five-story human towers would be featured in many Soka Gakkai culture festivals as a symbol of the unity of the youth division members. But this was not the end of the challenges that the youth took up. In March 1982, at the first Kansai Youth Peace Culture Festival held at the Nagai Track and Field Stadium in Osaka, a six-story human tower was erected. This remarkable accomplishment was an expression of the joy of life experienced by Soka youth.

The Tokyo Culture Festival was nearing its finale. The card stunt depicted famous scenes from around the world in bright colors, including New York's Statue of Liberty, San Francisco's Golden Gate Bridge, India's Taj Mahal, the Great Wall of China, the Arc de Triomphe and the Eiffel Tower of Paris, and the pyramids of Egypt.

Officials from forty-five embassies attended the culture festival, and when a scene from their country appeared, they applauded with even greater enthusiasm.

During this card stunt presentation, steel towers and a bridge were carried out onto the field, followed by a procession of all the performers. The young women's dancers, the young men's gymnastics teams, the high school gymnastics group, the members of the Fife and Drum Corps and the others all made their way spiritedly around the field. Smiling brightly with their heads held high, they waved yellow, green, red and blue flags as they went. It was a glorious march of triumphant youth.

The phrase *world peace* appeared in Japanese in the stands, and then changed to the equivalent in English, Russian, Spanish, Italian, French, Chinese, Hindi, Arabic and other languages. It even appeared in Vietnamese, for the people of that country who had been suffering from war for so long. The cards represented the strong and passionate commitment of Soka Gakkai members to work for peace.

THE PROCESSION moved around the field in a figure eight. A bridge set up at the juncture of the eight allowed one file of members to pass over the other. The members of the Ladder Brigade climbed atop the multitiered steel towers that had been posted in the center of each of the eight's loops and moved their upper bodies to create an image of undulating waves. The steel towers resembled crowns or large flowers. The card stunt displayed the Chinese characters for *world peace* in red against a gold backdrop, the calligraphy a duplication of Shin'ichi Yamamoto's writing of it.

A young woman fighting against a collagen disease

had been responsible for transferring Shin'ichi's writing to the miniature-scale seating chart of the stadium stands. As a result of her condition, her tear ducts were inflamed and no longer functioned, so she suffered from a constant sensation of dryness in her eyes, as if she had sand in them. She could barely produce saliva, and consequently also experienced mouth ulcers. Having studied design, however, when she heard about the Tokyo Culture Festival, she volunteered to assist with the card stunt.

The leaders in charge were concerned when they saw her frail condition, but she told them: "I want to take this on to challenge myself. It will be my own personal battle." For the next three months, she worked very hard, cutting back on sleep to stay on schedule and transfer the various designs, including Shin'ichi's calligraphy, to the seating charts. The task of coloring in the forty-two thousand squares per chart each day was a test of the limits of her mental and physical endurance. But in the end, her success in this endeavor served as a tremendous source of self-confidence for the rest of her life. She would later go on to overcome her illness and regain her health.

The culture festival was a triumph of youth, as each participant took on and surmounted his or her own personal limitations.

One of the members of the five-story human tower team was sent to Aichi Prefecture[2] by his company for a long business trip in September, a month before the culture festival. At first he thought he might have to give up participating, but he decided to challenge himself and commuted to rehearsals in Tokyo by bullet train. His example served as an inspiration to other members who felt physically exhausted or were having trouble balancing work and rehearsals.

In the end, they all won over themselves. They each emerged as a proud champion of the drama of their youth.

THE TOKYO CULTURE Festival, a magnificent, youthful dance of life, was reaching its conclusion. "Song of a New Age," the festival's theme song, echoed into the sky:

> *An age of new ideals*
> *now opens before us . . .*

The gold backdrop behind the red Chinese characters for *world peace* in the stands sparkled brilliantly in the sunlight.

World peace is not something given to us. It is something that we human beings must create, through our own effort and wisdom. It is something we must struggle for and win.

The key, therefore, to building peace is for individuals to develop themselves as human beings, and to challenge their weaknesses and triumph over them. In other words, peace can never be achieved without the struggle of human revolution, the struggle to develop and elevate our state of life.

Furthermore, if war is a realm of the fear of death, then peace must be a realm of the joy of life.

The participants in the Tokyo Culture Festival overflowed with the joy of life. Filled with such brilliance, the festival was a paean to humanity and the manifestation of the light of peace.

At 3:55 PM, the grand human drama of the culture festival came to an end amidst thunderous cheers and applause. Many of the guests gained a deeper understanding of and respect for the Soka Gakkai through the festival. Among them was the great Japanese industrialist Konosuke Matsushita, the founder of Panasonic, who later remarked to a *Seikyo Shimbun* reporter: "I felt the excitement the moment I set foot in the stadium. As the magnificent card stunt and field events unfolded, the entire arena was transformed into a giant work of art. I was moved by the dynamic performances and indescribable beauty I witnessed.

"Everyone was swept away by the participants' strong conviction welling forth from their profound faith. I myself was deeply impressed and gained a great deal from the experience."

The culture festival led to a series of meetings and correspondences between Matsushita and Shin'ichi Yamamoto, the latter of which were eventually compiled into a book titled *Jinsei Mondo* (Questions and Answers About Life).

One journalist who attended the event also observed: "Without a doubt, the culture festival's great success can be attributed to the Soka Gakkai's essential nature—that is, the voluntary cooperation of a large number of people toward a common goal."

WHEN ASKED his thoughts on the culture festival, a guest from the business community praised the efforts of the members who worked behind the scenes to make the festival possible, saying: "The performances were truly splendid, but I was particularly impressed by those working behind the scenes. Though it was a huge event, it was so well organized and executed that there wasn't a single piece of litter to be found anywhere around the stadium. I believe that such attention to detail and genuine concern for others only comes from deep religious commitment."

A column in the October 18 edition of the *Mainichi Shimbun,* one of Japan's leading daily newspapers, said of the culture festival: "Both inside and outside the stadium, the event was carried through with great organization. Getting off the train at nearby Sendagaya Station on the Chuo Line, I was greeted by young men who tipped their white sports caps and thanked me for coming as they directed me to the stadium. This may be expected behavior when one has been invited to an event, but it's still not a common experience these days."

Shin'ichi had shown tremendous concern for the members working as event staff for the culture festival. These were the members involved in such inconspicuous tasks as cleaning, directing traffic and preparing for the numerous programs. When the festival was over and he had said his thanks to the guests, he went to see the event staff youth who were busy at work around the stadium.

Shin'ichi regarded these young men and women as a great force behind the success of the Tokyo Culture

Festival. He waved and called out to them as they rushed about fulfilling their various responsibilities.

"Thank you for all your hard work!" Shin'ichi said. When they turned to look at him, their youthful faces were illuminated by the setting sun. Bowing deeply to a group of young women's members nearby who were busy sweeping, he then remarked: "Thank you! The culture festival has been a huge success thanks to your diligent efforts." The young women smiled happily as they returned his greetings and then resumed their work, all of them wonderful examples of youth dedicated to their mission.

Nichiren writes: "Where there is unseen virtue, there will be visible reward" (WND, 907). Whether or not we have great conviction in this determines our faith and our attainment of Buddhahood in this existence.

THAT EVENING, after the culture festival was cleaned up and everyone had gone home, the youth division leaders in charge of the event went to the Soka Gakkai Headquarters to make a final report to Shin'ichi Yamamoto. They were all in high spirits as they thanked him for his support.

"You did a fantastic job," Shin'ichi told them with a smile. "The festival was wonderful."

The leaders began to excitedly speak.

One said: "It was a great success! I don't think any other organization could have put on such an outstanding culture festival."

Another commented: "All of the guests were very impressed by it."

And a third said: "We were just talking about how a festival of such grand scale and excellence is unprecedented in the history of the Soka Gakkai."

As Shin'ichi listened to their remarks, his face gradually clouded over. He then asked the youth leader: "Did you make an effort to express your gratitude to the support staff who cleaned up?"

"No," the leader admitted.

Shin'ichi could see that these top leaders of the youth, intoxicated by the festival's success, had unconsciously allowed pride and complacency to take root in their hearts. His stern rebuke rang through the room: "You're all very pleased with yourselves, aren't you?"

They stared silently at Shin'ichi.

"While you were all busy patting yourselves on the back for your great success, I was giving my all to encouraging those members working hard to clean up the stadium grounds and directing traffic. The culture festival was a success precisely because of their behind-the-scenes efforts.

"The Tokyo Culture Festival is over and done with now. If you become drunk on your past achievements, all that awaits you is defeat. It's vital that you keep your guard up even after a victory and continue to move forward without pause. If you forget this spirit, you will grow arrogant and careless, and everything will fall apart."

To the last moment, Shin'ichi put his whole heart into training the youth involved in the culture festival, which served as a great opportunity for personal development. Sensing Shin'ichi's boundless hopes for them in his stern words, the youth leaders were deeply moved.

ON OCTOBER 30, 1967, Shin'ichi Yamamoto received a guest from Europe at the Soka Culture Center in Shinano-machi, Tokyo—a silver-haired gentleman with a healthy glow and a dignified and gentle expression. His name was Count Richard Coudenhove-Kalergi, a leading proponent of European unification.

The guest's eyes sparkled as he said: "I am overjoyed to have the opportunity to meet you, President Yamamoto, a practitioner of the great world religion of Nichiren Buddhism and leader of a peace movement based on that teaching. I would like to express my deep respect for you."

Count Coudenhove-Kalergi had arrived in Japan four days earlier, on October 26, at the joint invitation of NHK, Japan Broadcasting Corporation, a peace studies institute founded by the president of one of Japan's largest construction companies, and other organizations.

The main purpose of his visit was to attend a ceremony at which the peace institute would bestow upon him its first peace prize.

Count Coudenhove-Kalergi had been born in Japan, but returned with his family to his father's homeland of what was then Austria-Hungary soon after his birth. For the seventy-two-year-old Count, this trip was thus a kind of homecoming after an interval of seventy-one years. His father, Heinrich, had been a member of the European nobility and a diplomat for the Austro-Hungarian Empire. While residing in Japan as his nation's charge d'affaires, he met and married a Japanese woman named Mitsuko. Their marriage was a celebrated international romance in Japan during a time when the country was beginning to modernize after almost three centuries of virtual seclusion.

Heinrich and Mitsuko had two children while residing in Tokyo. The second of their sons, born in 1894 and given the Japanese name Eijiro, was Richard Coudenhove-Kalergi. The family soon moved to Austria-Hungary, where Heinrich died ten years later. By that time, he and Mitsuko had seven children.

Though Richard lost his father when he was young, he was still greatly influenced by him. Heinrich had been a truly cosmopolitan figure who opposed anti-Semitism, loved Asia, had a profound understanding of Arab and Indian cultures, and spoke eighteen languages. When taking his children on strolls, he would talk to them about the customs and history of countries around the world. Richard learned the spirit of peace and a global perspective from his father.

AT THE AGE OF TWENTY-EIGHT, Count Coudenhove-Kalergi published a book titled *Pan-Europe* and began working toward European unification, becoming an active advocate of peace. When his trip to Japan was decided, the Count expressed to the organizations that had invited him a strong desire to meet Shin'ichi Yamamoto. He was not only interested in Buddhism because it was his mother's religion, but he had also taken note of and studied the Soka Gakkai as a rapidly developing lay Buddhist organization firmly established among the people. The vigorous activities of Soka Gakkai members aimed at alleviating the sufferings of others through the teachings of Buddhism had left a deep impression on him.

In an interview he gave in Paris to the *Tokyo Shimbun* newspaper before arriving in Japan, he said: "In the Buddhist world, a new renaissance is growing as Buddhism awakens from a long sleep. . . . In Japan, for example, the spread of a movement called the Soka Gakkai is being reported. I believe this signifies a revival of Buddhism, which was the world's first fraternal movement."[3]

In using the word *fraternal*, the Count was referring in European concepts to the Soka Gakkai as a movement based on Buddhist compassion. He keenly perceived that the genuine spirit and practice of Buddhism were alive in the Soka Gakkai, and had developed a strong interest in Shin'ichi Yamamoto as the organization's leader.

Including Shin'ichi, Count Coudenhove-Kalergi requested meetings with seven figures—Emperor Hirohito, Crown Prince Akihito, Prime Minister Eisaku Sato, Foreign Minister Takeo Miki and others.

Shin'ichi readily consented to a meeting with the Count. He knew that mutual understanding and friendship could only come about through face-to-face encounters. Dialogue has the power to bring people together and unite them.

As a Buddhist and a human being, Shin'ichi had decided that he must search out and discover the path to lasting peace for all humanity, and he believed that the exchange of thoughts and wisdom through dialogue was indispensable to realizing that aim.

S HIN'ICHI WAS RESOLVED to build an international network of people of wisdom and strong determination who sought peace—a network transcending national and ethnic boundaries. Though Count Coudenhove-Kalergi may have been culturally influenced by his Japanese mother, Shin'ichi was certain that his dialogue with him would be an exchange between Eastern and Western civilizations. He deeply respected the Count and hoped to humbly learn more of the convictions, philosophy and experiences of this pioneer in the movement for European unification.

On October 30, Shin'ichi met Count Coudenhove-Kalergi and his party outside the entranceway to the Soka Culture Center in Shinano-machi, Tokyo.

"Thank you for coming," he said. "I am honored to meet you, and I welcome you with all my heart."

From the moment they shook hands, Shin'ichi felt as if he was being reunited with an old friend. This was no doubt because he had read most of his guest's books as well as other materials about him that had been translated into Japanese, and he felt a strong resonance with the Count's positions, ideas and way of life.

Coudenhove-Kalergi was accompanied to his meeting with Shin'ichi by staff members of NHK. The first topic of their discussion, which took place through the aid of interpreters, was the role that Japan should play in achieving world peace.

The Count said: "I believe that the most important thing is for Japan to take initiative in efforts to realize peace. The curtain opened on the nuclear age about two decades ago and now many nations of the world are preparing for the next war.

"Amid this reality, in addition to having one of the strongest economies in the world, Japan has its peace constitution, an unparalleled document in the world. Another important precedent is that, until the modern era began, Japan enjoyed three centuries of peace both at home and abroad. Furthermore, modern Japanese culture is a harmonious blend of Western civilization, Confucianism and Buddhism.

"Considering all these factors, I think that Japan must show leadership for the rest of the world in the quest for peace."

"THAT'S A VERY IMPORTANT perspective," Shin'ichi remarked. "I completely concur."

Shin'ichi found himself in full agreement with Count Coudenhove-Kalergi's ideas. He, too, was keenly aware of the gravity of Japan's mission in the world as the only nation with a constitution outlawing war. The ideals of pacifism and international cooperation were clearly articulated in the preamble and Article 9 of Japan's constitution. In the first clause of this article, the constitution renounced the nation's right to wage war, voluntarily restricting its national sovereignty. Shin'ichi felt that this article contained the constitution's intent to relegate a portion of Japan's sovereignty to the United Nations and other international institutions. In other words, he sensed that it encompassed the ideal of a united world.

Shin'ichi regarded the constitution as the supreme treasure of the Japanese people. He was personally determined to devote his life to the actualization of humanity's fervent wish of an end to all war, as expressed in Article 9, for that itself is an important goal of Buddhist practitioners. And he had concluded that spreading the ideal and spirit of peace articulated in the Japanese constitution throughout the world was the direction the country should take as it made its way toward the twenty-first century.

From the outset, the dialogue between Shin'ichi and Coudenhove-Kalergi went right to the heart of matters.

Shin'ichi was delighted to meet and talk with the Count. He considered this man—eagerly seeking the means to achieve world peace—to be a true comrade.

Shin'ichi said: "Today, I would like to ask you several questions as a representative of Japan's youth—for the sake of Japan's future as a civilized nation, and more, for the cause of world peace."

His first question was whether Coudenhove-Kalergi agreed that it was necessary to further expand the concept of European unification in order to achieve lasting peace. He also offered his frank opinion that the Western European approach of completely rejecting communism was likely to increase the tension between the Western and Eastern blocs, thereby making the realization of peace impossible, and he asked his guest for his thoughts on these subjects.

INITIALLY, THE DIALOGUE progressed with Coudenhove-Kalergi responding to Shin'ichi Yamamoto's questions, but it wasn't long before he took over and began asking his host various questions.

"Will the Soka Gakkai's movement to revive the spirit of Buddhism be limited to Japan, or will it spread throughout the world?" he inquired.

"It will definitely not be limited to Japan," Shin'ichi replied. "Our aim is to realize peace and happiness for all humanity based on the teachings of Nichiren. The

Buddhist concept of compassion for others and of the dignity and equality of all life—that all people inherently possess the unsurpassed life-state of Buddhahood—are indispensable to the attainment of world peace.

"We consider the widespread communication of this humanistic philosophy, a common treasure of all humanity, to be the mission of the Soka Gakkai."

"I see," Coudenhove-Kalergi replied. "The reason for my question is that I have frequently heard criticisms of the Soka Gakkai as an ethnocentric or nationalist organization."

Smiling, Shin'ichi said: "There are people who regard Nichiren as a nationalist or a proponent of Japanese supremacy, but such views are fundamentally mistaken. They have been created through the erroneous interpretation of Nichiren Buddhism by so-called Nichirenists and their misguided words and actions. In reality, however, Nichiren's own assertion that the leader of the military government of his day was 'the ruler of this little island country' (WND 765) attests to the fact that his concerns transcended the boundaries of the Japanese state to encompass the happiness of all humanity.

"Further, in thirteenth-century Japan, he declared that the teachings of the Lotus Sutra would be 'spread abroad widely throughout Jambudvipa' (WND, 400). Jambudvipa refers to the entire world. This completely contradicts any narrow-minded notions that restrict his attentions to a single nation. In exact accord with his spirit, the Soka Gakkai has spread a movement of Buddhist humanism across the globe."

Count Coudenhove-Kalergi nodded in understanding

as he listened to Shin'ichi speak. He then remarked: "I am very glad I can confirm that the Soka Gakkai is not a nationalistic movement. I am sure your organization will make an important contribution to the world."

THE COUNT CONTINUED with a number of questions: "How many members does the Soka Gakkai have around the world?" "Are they Japanese or local people?" He went on to ask in detail about the membership and activities in war-torn Vietnam as well as in other countries, such as Cambodia and France.

After responding to each of his guest's questions, Shin'ichi began to speak about Buddhism: "Buddhism is an eternal and unchanging law that pervades human life and the entire universe. It is also the guiding principle for the realization of peace and happiness for humanity. As such, it in no way contradicts modern science. Rather, it is a philosophy that can lead science and technology in a direction that will contribute to people's happiness and well-being.

"Our movement aims for what we call human revolution, the inner transformation of the individual through the teachings of Nichiren Buddhism. Society is made up of human beings; we are the creators of our reality. As a result, we believe that by cultivating our lives, our hearts, we can change society. The purpose of the Soka Gakkai is to help people forge their character on a fundamental level, thereby bringing the fragrant flowers of peace and culture to bloom. We emphasize the view that all things arise from the human heart, the human spirit."

Coudenhove-Kalergi nodded to show his agreement

and said: "That's very important. I believe in the universal validity of Buddhism, a teaching that transcends time and accords with science. I regard the revival of Buddhism in Japan by the Soka Gakkai as Japan's response to the materialism that dominates our world, and I think this marks the beginning of a new age in the history of religion."

Looking intently at Shin'ichi, the Count then added in a voice filled with emotion: "I am aware that, in addition to being under constant attack, you are struggling against many opponents in and outside Japan. But this is true of all great people. In your case, however, even your opponents cannot fail to recognize what a gifted leader you are."

THE FACT WAS that at the time, the Soka Gakkai and Shin'ichi Yamamoto were frequent targets of criticism and abuse both domestically and abroad. Coudenhove-Kalergi, who had been persecuted and forced into exile for his opposition to the Nazis, knew only too well the fate of one who dared to stand up for the cause of truth and justice.

Shin'ichi replied with calm resolve: "You have said that I am struggling against many opponents around the world, but I would like to make clear that I do not regard people as opponents just because they uphold different ideologies or religions. Of course violence and terrorism are absolute evils, and I will always challenge authorities that try to dominate and subjugate the people.

"But philosophies and religions that seek to bring happiness to the people and alleviate their suffering share a common belief in the value of human life. As long as that belief exists, I'm certain that differing ideologies can find grounds for communication and sympathy and that mutual understanding is possible. In addition, the Buddhist teaching that all people equally possess the Buddha nature taps into a universal inner realm pervading all life.

"I believe that if humanity focuses on this point and concentrates on what we share as human beings, we will be able to shift our mental orientation from divisiveness to harmony. I also think that we need to not simply recognize the cultural differences that emerge from various religions, but to respect them."

Coudenhove-Kalergi conveyed his full agreement. His eyes shone and a carefree smile spread across his face. As a person actively searching for a way to end religious conflict, it may have been that Shin'ichi's words gave him new inspiration.

Their conversation continued, covering such topics as Western philosophy and Buddhist thought, the United Nations and the Vietnam War. Soon an hour had passed and it was time for them to end. Count Coudenhove-Kalergi reluctantly rose from his seat. It had been a fruitful discussion, but Shin'ichi, too, still had many subjects and questions he wished to explore with the Count. They shook hands firmly and promised to meet again.

ON NOVEMBER 18, Shin'ichi Yamamoto received a cordial letter of thanks from Count Coudenhove-Kalergi, who had returned to Europe. In it, the Count had written: "My meeting with you was the most valuable encounter of my visit to Japan. I would like to send my praises for your brilliant accomplishments as well as express my earnest hope that the Buddhist renaissance you are carrying out, for which I have the greatest respect, will positively influence the future course of not only Japan but Asia and the rest of the world."

Coudenhove-Kalergi's high expectations for the Soka Gakkai revitalized Shin'ichi's resolve to work for world peace. He immediately composed a reply to the Count, inviting him to visit Japan three years hence. His letter concluded: "I am aware that it is the Soka Gakkai's supreme mission to realize lasting peace and a world free of war and weapons of annihilation through the Buddhist renaissance to which you refer, as well as through our cooperation with other pacifist forces worldwide. And I am increasingly determined that we will fulfill that mission.

"I pray with all my heart that you may live long and continue to write your important works and carry out your significant activities, and I look forward to the day when we will meet again."

Nine months after their meeting, Coudenhove-Kalergi published an account of his visit to Japan entitled *Bi no Kuni—Nihon e no Kikyo* ("Land of Beauty—Return to My Birthplace, Japan"). In this work, he wrote his impressions of Shin'ichi Yamamoto, stating: "I was struck by the dynamism of this man of just thirty-nine years. He is a born leader. He is not someone silently seated in meditation. He is a person filled with joie de vivre and vibrant energy. He is honest, friendly and furthermore extremely intelligent. . . . Our meeting was one of the most enjoyable events of my stay in Tokyo."[4]

Correspondence between Shin'ichi and Coudenhove-Kalergi continued for some time. They later decided to publish a dialogue on the theme of Eastern and Western civilization, which would take place on the Count's next visit to Japan.

COUNT COUDENHOVE-KALERGI and Shin'-ichi Yamamoto met again in October 1970. The first session of this, their second encounter, took place on October 7 at the Soka Culture Center in Shinano-machi, Tokyo, and lasted about three hours. On October 17, following a lecture by the Count titled "My Life" at the Soka Junior High School and Soka High School (both opened in Tokyo in 1968), the two spoke again for another four hours. Then, on the 25th and 26th, they held another meeting at the newly opened Seikyo Shim-bun building. In total, their dialogue took place over the course of more than ten hours.

Shin'ichi approached their exchange with the desire to offer direction for young people as they headed toward the twenty-first century. Their talks were organized around a number of topics and issues presented by Shin'-ichi, beginning with a discussion of Japan and moving on to various other subjects that included the international situation, the United Nations, nationalism, the relationship of humanity and nature, environmental pollution, the revival of religion, leadership ideals, the culture of the Pacific region, democracy, respect for the sanctity of life, youth, women and education. The underlying goal pervading the entire dialogue was how to realize world peace.

Count Coudenhove-Kalergi remarked: "I believe the only way to avoid a third world war is to transcend all differences of ethnicity, religion, ideology and nationality through some sort of spiritual movement and collectively achieve a recognition of the importance of peaceful coexistence and mutual human trust."[5]

Shin'ichi replied: "The philosophical foundation that I have been emphasizing is exactly that kind of spiritual movement. No matter how favorable circumstances become for peaceful coexistence, without a means by which to sublimate antagonism between nations, a third world war may be inevitable. I believe that we must forge something within our lives that enables us to transcend conflict and opposition. . . .

"In other words, we need to establish a universal awareness that we are all global citizens. I believe your Pan-European movement has contributed to this cause. Pan-Europeanism, in my opinion, is a step toward an internationalism that will link all the world's people."[6]

"I agree completely," Count Coudenhove-Kalergi remarked.

Their dialogue was a spiritual exchange shining with brilliant wisdom that could illuminate the darkness shrouding humanity.

COUNT COUDENHOVE-KALERGI, who described Japan as "an independent 'continent' in the Pacific with its own distinct civilization," conveyed high expectations for the country.

He spoke with fervor as he said to Shin'ichi: "It is crucial for Japan to present a great philosophy to the world.

I believe the time has arrived. That great philosophy is the pacifist and life-affirming religion of Buddhism, a teaching that originated in India, passed through China and reached its culmination in Japan."[7]

This was no doubt the Count's ardent wish.

Shin'ichi regarded these words as Count Coudenhove-Kalergi's injunction to him. The source of contemporary society's suffering was the absence of a fundamental appreciation for the sanctity of human life. Without such appreciation, humanity would never be restored to a state of genuine dignity.

To respect the sanctity of life means that people's right to live, their individuality and their right to happiness are not sacrificed for anything. Without the worldwide spread of a great philosophy supporting this truth, humanity will never enjoy real happiness or peace. Count Coudenhove-Kalergi must have keenly understood this.

Shin'ichi replied emphatically: "The issue you have brought up is something that I have earnestly grappled with. I am determined to continue working hard throughout my life to see that such a philosophy is communicated across the globe—for the sake of peace and the happiness of humankind."

A broad, deep smile spread across the Count's face.

Their dialogue was carried in one of Japan's leading business dailies, the *Sankei Shimbun,* as a series entitled "Bummei: Nishi to Higashi" or "Civilization: West and East" for six months starting in February 1971. It appeared twice weekly, in fifty-three installments. In 1972, Sankei Shimbun Publishing released it in book form under the same title as the newspaper series.[8]

People who read the dialogue were surprised to learn that a respected world thinker held the Soka Gakkai in high esteem, and Soka Gakkai members felt that the age when the sun of Nichiren Buddhism would shine the light of hope throughout the world had at last arrived.

NOTES

1. Yamato: Ancient name of Japan.

2. Aichi Prefecture: located approximately 220 miles southwest of Tokyo.

3. Translated from the September 23, 1967, evening edition of the *Tokyo Shimbun.*

4. Translated from Japanese. Count Richard Coudenhove-Kalergi, *Bi no Kuni—Nihon e no Kikyo,* translated by Morinosuke Kajima (Tokyo: Kajima Kenkyujo Shuppankai, 1968), pp. 93–96.

5. Translated from Japanese. Daisaku Ikeda and Richard Coudenhove-Kalergi, *Bummei: Nishi to Higashi* (Civilization: West and East) (Tokyo: Seikyo Shimbunsha, 1975), p. 114. Available only in Japanese.

6. Ibid., pp. 114–15.

7. Ibid., p. 249.

8. Seikyo Shimbunsha later published the same book in paperback.

Glorious Future

My fellow Bodhisattvas of the Earth,
comrades in faith—
now, at the dawn of the Century of Life,
our network has unfolded
across the globe.

In the recent past
of our history,
we experienced
days of harsh winds,
nights of raging waves,

and long years of harsh criticism
while we quietly kept our own council.

My dear friends—
on this morning of a new year
let us draw a line
and say farewell
to those days
of vicissitude and suffering.

My fellow Bodhisattvas of the Earth,
champions of the Mystic Law—
lift your heads and stand tall
on this truly glorious
morning of departure.

THIS POEM by President Yamamoto started off the Soka Gakkai's Year of Glory, 1968. Titled "On Our Departure Toward a Glorious Future," it covered the entire front page of the New Year's Day edition of the *Seikyo Shimbun.* Members pored over it with great intensity as if to engrave every word in their hearts.

Two years earlier, in 1966, Shin'ichi had composed a poem titled "Dawn" under the pen name Shin'ichio for the children's magazine *Friends of Hope,* published by the Soka Gakkai–affiliated Ushio Publishing Company. When members saw it, they began to call the Soka Gakkai Headquarters requesting that President Yamamoto write a poem for the *Seikyo Shimbun* as well. Shin'ichi also received several requests from the newspaper itself to contribute a poem to its New Year's edition.

Shin'ichi strongly felt that the Year of Glory would be a very important time in determining the future of kosen-rufu. The Soka Gakkai was now moving forward with all its activities focused on the long-awaited completion of the Grand Main Temple in 1972. With construction on the building about to begin, this year would be crucial in laying the foundation for the organization's success in the ensuing five years. It was a period in which they could not afford setbacks or failures.

Shin'ichi was determined to do anything to help the members advance with courage. He therefore composed this poem to mark the commencement of their decisive struggle together.

S HIN'ICHI recorded his honest sentiments regarding the start of the Year of Glory in his poem. The words flowed from his pen—conveying his boundless joy, passionate fighting spirit and love for his fellow members. As he wrote, he bid them in his heart to rise up, not to be defeated and to proceed in unity.

In the poem's opening lines, Shin'ichi called the twenty-first century the "Century of Life." By this he meant an age when life would be considered by all as infinitely precious, never exploited or sacrificed for any cause. It was an age of the restoration of human dignity. The transition from the twentieth century—a century characterized by war and atrocity—to a twenty-first century of peace and respect for life was indeed the aim of the Soka Gakkai's movement for kosen-rufu.

Shin'ichi had decided that this was his life's purpose, and he regarded the five years from 1968 through 1972 as the period for building the foundation for achieving that goal. It was therefore crucial that the Year of Glory, the start of that period, be a year of great victory.

The poem took shape in just fifteen minutes. Shin'ichi then went back and polished it over and over with great care. When at last he was finished, he was exhausted; he had poured his entire being into its composition. Nichiren states: "Words manifest through sound to convey the sentiments in our heart" (GZ, 563). In accord with this spirit, Shin'ichi's work pulsed with his fervent desire and determination for peace.

When "On Our Departure Toward a Glorious Future" was published, members across Japan telephoned and sent letters to the *Seikyo Shimbun* and the Soka Gakkai Headquarters expressing their appreciation.

One member who phoned said with great emotion: "I was electrified and overjoyed when I read it." Another wrote that the poem was "a fresh spring breeze of encouragement," while another called it a "gift of hope."

This single poem roused a symphonic chorus of the resolve to realize peace throughout the country in the New Year. All who read it deeply felt the profundity of their mission, and the Year of Glory thus began on a high note.

SHIN'ICHI YAMAMOTO loved poetry from the time he was a boy. In the world of poetry, he found that the wings of imagination carried his dreams freely through the heavens. He also felt that poetry was filled with endlessly profound, all-embracing, broad significance, and that it bloomed with the fragrant flowers of the heart. It was these qualities of poetry that had captured Shin'ichi's mind.

As he grew up and observed the way of the world and how people allowed themselves to grow cold and unfeeling, he began to sense the importance of rejuvenating the poetic spirit in people's hearts. It was a time when people, while on the one hand being oppressed by systems and institutions, were on the other consumed by materialism, and an excessive reliance on science and rationalism was robbing them of their spirituality. With each passing year, Shin'ichi regarded the revival of the poetic spirit—the construction of a rich spiritual realm in people's hearts—with ever-increasing urgency.

Shin'ichi believed that Nichiren Buddhism, which teaches the principles of a single life-moment encompassing three thousand realms and the interconnectedness of the universe and the self, was an inexhaustible wellspring of such a profound and vast poetic spirit. He also came to the conclusion that kosen-rufu, a movement to spread the ideals of Nichiren Buddhism, served the same purpose through its cultivation of the human spirit. Thus, as a poet striving for humanity's triumph, he composed "On Our Departure Toward a Glorious Future." This was the start of Shin'ichi's intense lifelong struggle of poetic creation.

He contributed two other poems to the *Seikyo Shimbun* that year. On January 8, the newspaper carried "Bathed in the Sunlight of Time Without Beginning," describing the mission and spirit of youth. And on the 9th, it carried "To the Guardians of the Dignity of Life," praising the nobility of women. Beginning with this year, he regularly contributed a poem to the newspaper's New Year's edition. In 1969, it was "Song of Building," and in 1970, "Sounds of Innovation."

The English word *poem* comes from the Greek *poesis,* meaning "creation." Shin'ichi's poetic endeavors were a struggle of words aimed at creating a century of life.

THE GREATEST HOPE and joy of Soka Gakkai members greeting the new Year of Glory was the opening of the Soka Junior High School and Soka High School. On April 8, 1968, the long-anticipated first entrance ceremony for the schools was held at the campus in Kodaira in Tokyo's Musashino region.[1]

Clear blue skies stretched over Musashino from the morning. As the students passed through the school gate wearing their brand new navy blue uniforms and hats, their faces shone with hope in the spring sunlight. The auditorium where the ceremony would be conducted was situated to the left, just inside the main entrance. Next to it rose a pristine white clock tower. The classrooms were housed in two modern four-story buildings, and the tree-covered campus evoked a feeling of old Musashino.

The area in front of the auditorium was filled with parents who had gathered there from early morning. Numerous conversations were going on and a mix of regional dialects could be heard. The entering students were from all over Japan—including Kyushu and Okinawa in the south, and Tohoku and Hokkaido in the north.

One mother had tears in her eyes as she gazed up at the clock tower. Whispering to her husband, she said:

"The campus is so spacious and green, and the buildings are beautiful. It's like a dream that our child can study at this school founded by President Yamamoto."

Her husband smiled broadly and nodded as he said: "That's right. It was worth every effort, too. It's going to be a challenge to send our son to school in Tokyo, but since he said he would do his very best, we have to work hard to support him."

"I'll do my best, too," the mother replied. "He's lucky to be born at such a significant time."

When the parents were finally shown inside the auditorium, they gasped at its splendor. More than twelve hundred seats were arranged in ascending rows, and the ceiling was designed in an undulating wave pattern to maximize acoustics. It was a magnificent venue, rivaling the most famous theaters in Tokyo.

The parents were delighted to know that their children would be learning in such an environment every day.

ONCE ALL the parents were seated in the auditorium, the students made their entrance to the strains of "Grand March" from Richard Wagner's opera *Tannhäuser*. They were fresh and spirited as they strode in proudly wearing their school uniforms. The sight of them triggered spontaneous applause from the parents, many of who dabbed their tears.

After everyone had practiced singing the school song once together, Vice Principal Fumitaka Morotani announced the start of the entrance ceremony just before ten o'clock in the morning. Morotani was a thirty-two-year-old social studies teacher who had formerly worked at a Tokyo metropolitan high school. His remarks were followed by greetings from Principal Takashi Oyamada, who was forty-four and a science doctorate. While engaged in biological research at Tokyo University of Education, he taught night courses at another Tokyo high school for sixteen years. As principal and vice principal, Oyamada and Morotani were in charge of the operation of the new Soka Junior High School and Soka High School.

Oyamada announced that there were 217 junior high students and 321 high school students entering the schools in the first year. Smiling, he said in a warm tone that revealed his personality: "I would like to offer my sincere congratulations to our entering students and their parents. Before the opening of our school, we received the following five guidelines from our founder, President Yamamoto:

1. Become people who seek the truth, create value and possess wisdom and enthusiasm.
2. Do not cause trouble to others and always take responsibility for your own actions.
3. Be considerate and polite, reject violence and value trustworthiness and cooperation.
4. Boldly speak out for your beliefs and act courageously for the sake of truth and justice.
5. Cultivate an enterprising spirit and become respectable leaders of Japan and the world.

"I think many of you are already aware of these five points, which were outlined in remarks made by President

Yamamoto published in the April 4 edition of the *Seikyo Shimbun* under the headline "Celebrating the Soka Schools' Entrance Ceremony." They offer a clear indication of our path of advancement. I hope you will all take these guidelines to heart and make your years at the Soka schools meaningful."

IN HIS REMARKS, Shin'ichi had discussed the purpose of establishing the Soka Junior High School and Soka High School, stating: "It goes without saying that the Soka schools have not been established for the sake of the Soka Gakkai. The Soka Gakkai's goal is to create a vibrant 'third civilization' and everlasting human prosperity based on the solid foundation of Nichiren's teachings.

"The Soka schools exist solely for the purpose of education and will thus aim to produce excellent results in that regard. In fact, there is no religious education in the schools' curriculum, and many of the students are not Soka Gakkai members. I wish to declare that the Soka schools seek to do nothing more than foster talented people who can shoulder the future of Japan and contribute to the betterment of the world."

Shin'ichi went on to address the causes of the prevailing atmosphere of confusion afflicting the realm of education in Japan at the time. He pointed to the loss of educational ideals, the tendency to disregard the individuality of young people and the lack of a sense of responsibility among leaders in regard to the next generation. He further expressed his hope that teachers, students and parents would unite in a continuous and concrete effort to realize an ideal system of education through the new schools that would provide direction for the entire educational arena.

Lastly, he remarked: "Nothing could give me more joy than to see the emergence from our schools of countless intelligent youth eager to build a new century who will contribute to the peace and prosperity of Japan and the world."

As he closed his speech, Principal Takashi Oyamada stressed: "It is the wish of President Yamamoto, our schools' founder, that all of you will develop into people who can contribute to the welfare of Japan and the world. I hope you will have pride in your role as the first classes of the Soka schools and that you will be excellent students and establish a fine tradition for those who follow in your footsteps.

"I would like to end my speech today by expressing my wish that you will respect each other, diligently study together and exert yourselves with the dynamic energy of youth, thereby developing yourselves as human beings."

Having gathered that day in great anticipation, the students' eyes shone with excitement. Next, a student representative made a pledge on behalf of both classes: "When we learned of the opening of Soka Junior High School and Soka High School, an event that heralds the arrival of a new age, we were awakened to a significant new goal and studied day and night in order to gain acceptance."

THE VOICE of the student reading the pledge rang with hope: "We firmly pledge on the happy occasion of this entrance ceremony that, in this splendid environment, we will train ourselves mentally and physically, devote ourselves to our studies, and become people who will actively work for world peace in the future."

The young man's face as he spoke shone with determination to fulfill his mission, and his heart beat with youthful verve and resolve to study hard and develop himself.

Kazumasa Morikawa, the general director of the Soka schools' board of directors, next took the podium. He related the events leading to the schools' establishment and conveyed his hopes for the growth of the new students. Lastly, everyone sang the school song together.

Though President Yamamoto had not attended the ceremony, everyone felt his high expectations and consideration for the schools in the remarks made by the principal, general director and guests. The jubilant entrance ceremony came to an end at 10:45 AM.

When it was over, General Director Morikawa took the microphone and announced in an excited voice: "I'm happy to report that President Yamamoto just left the Soka Gakkai Headquarters in Shinano-machi and is on his way here. He should be here in about an hour."

Cheers and applause filled the auditorium. Both the students and their parents had hoped that they might encounter President Yamamoto at the entrance ceremony. Shin'ichi understood their feelings well, but he also believed that the operation of the schools should be entrusted to the principal, general director and other faculty and board members. To make that clear, he had decided that as founder it was most appropriate for him to offer his support from the sidelines instead of taking center stage.

That was also why Shin'ichi had declined to attend the reception celebrating the schools' opening held on campus on March 16 with five hundred guests. He waited until the main event was over and then visited the campus to encourage the teachers and school staff. General Director Morikawa had pleaded with him to attend the entrance ceremony, but Shin'ichi firmly declined.

SHIN'ICHI YAMAMOTO said to Kazumasa Morikawa: "I'd like you, as the schools' general director, to work together with Principal Oyamada and the other faculty to take full responsibility for managing the schools. I hope you will make every effort to ensure as quickly as possible that the schools can operate on their own.

"A school's founder is like a needle; the general director and principal are like the thread. The needle may begin the process of stitching together an article of clothing, but it's the thread that holds the piece together. With this awareness, I'd like you to see that the schools make an independent start. That's why I'm not going to attend the entrance ceremony.

"I will, however, visit the campus later in the day to encourage the students and their parents in my capacity as the schools' founder."

Morikawa looked relieved.

Shin'ichi continued: "Despite the fact that the students could have attended any number of famous, top-notch schools, they have chosen to attend the schools I founded even though these schools have yet to build a reputation. And their families are willing to do everything they can to support them. I'm sure it's going to be financially difficult for many of them—especially those coming from outlying areas.

"But they are determined to join me in realizing the educational ideals set forth by President Makiguchi and President Toda. I feel tremendous appreciation for them. The Soka schools students are my priceless treasures. They are my life. They are my precious children. I will protect them no matter what. I will fight on their behalf to the end. That is my personal resolve.

"Even so, I want you to take on the task of running the schools without me. I'd like you to work hard with a steadfast personal commitment to help every single student develop into a great talent ready to shoulder the future of the world. The principal, teachers and general director must lead the way. The famous Japanese writer Eiji Yoshikawa wrote a poem that says it all: '*The chrysanthemum grower / stays in the shadows / when the chrysanthemum blossom is viewed.*' This describes my sentiments perfectly—now that the schools are founded, I would prefer to remain in the shadows."

Morikawa listened quietly as Shin'ichi spoke, sensing his immense and passionate dedication to the schools.

WHILE the entrance ceremony was taking place, Shin'ichi Yamamoto left Shinano-machi by car and headed for the Soka schools campus. He was overcome with emotion to think that this day had finally arrived. His mind filled with thoughts from the occasion when his mentor Josei Toda had entrusted him with this mission.

President Toda had first spoken to Shin'ichi about establishing a school in the late autumn of 1950. It was around the time that Toda's businesses had collapsed and together they were setting forth on a new and difficult path. Toda told Shin'ichi how President Makiguchi had charged him with the cherished goal of establishing a comprehensive school system providing education from elementary school through the university level.

Toda said to Shin'ichi: "If I cannot do this during my lifetime, I ask you to do it in yours. I want you to make sure that a superb educational environment is offered at the school that President Makiguchi long dreamed of."

At that moment, Shin'ichi firmly pledged in his heart that no matter what, as President Toda's disciple, he would found a school for value-creating education. While Toda had entrusted this project to Shin'ichi, he rarely spoke of it to anyone else.

On one occasion, Katsu Kiyohara said to Toda: "I think that the Soka Gakkai needs to establish an institution to carry out President Makiguchi's value-creating education. Shall we start a school like Jishu Gakkan?"[2]

President Toda replied sternly: "Don't concern yourself with that!"

Puzzled by this response, Kiyohara gave it some thought. She realized that President Toda had neither agreed nor disagreed with her remark; he just told her not to concern herself with it. *No doubt he had a plan of his own*, she thought.

In later years, when Kiyohara heard Shin'ichi announce

the intention to establish a university and high school, she finally understood the full meaning of Toda's words that day. *At that time,* she thought, *President Yamamoto had already been entrusted with this project by President Toda and was steadily drawing up a plan and making preparations toward its accomplishment. The wheels of construction had already been set in motion between mentor and disciple.*

AFTER JOSEI TODA'S DEATH, Shin'ichi Yamamoto, as the sole general administrator of the Soka Gakkai, was for all practical purposes entirely responsible for the organization's operations. From then, he began to search in earnest for land on which to build a high school. He had four requirements for the site: one, it should be located in Musashino, a region in western Tokyo known for its natural beauty; two, Mount Fuji should be visible; three, there should be a clean waterway flowing nearby; and four, it should be within about an hour's drive from central Tokyo.

He was shown a piece of land that met these conditions in Kodaira City, near Takanodai Station on the Seibu Kokubunji Line. It was a quiet location about 8.16 acres in an area not far from the Tamagawa Aqueduct. Shin'ichi went to see the land on April 5, 1960—a month before he became the third president of the Soka Gakkai. At the time, he was still declining requests that he take on that responsibility, but gradually the insistent entreaties of the top Soka Gakkai leadership were making it increasingly difficult to refuse.

Shin'ichi wanted to wait until at least the sixth anniversary of President Toda's death in 1964, but as Toda's disciple, he was also resolved to stand up and lead the organization. Thinking about what his first action should be to realize the ideals of his predecessors and to open the way toward eternal peace for humanity, he decided to begin with taking practical steps toward establishing a school.

On that early spring day, Shin'ichi and his wife, Mineko, left their home in Kobayashi-cho, Ota Ward, in a car provided by the Soka Gakkai Headquarters and headed toward the possible site for the school. The surrounding area was wooded with sawtooth oaks, magnolias, willows, camphor trees and peach trees, while the fields were abloom with mustard flowers. It was a refreshing and peaceful natural setting that fulfilled all of Shin'ichi's requirements. It seemed the perfect educational environment.

"This is it," he decided. "Here's where we'll build the school!"

Sitting in a little grove of trees near the banks of the aqueduct, Shin'ichi and Mineko ate the rice balls that Mineko had prepared for them. As they took turns sipping tea from the cap of a thermos bottle, they talked.

"It's a fine place," Shin'ichi said. "I'm sure President Makiguchi and President Toda would be very happy if we built a school here."

MINEKO LISTENED as Shin'ichi spoke, and then remarked in a concerned tone: "Building a school costs a lot of money. The Soka Gakkai doesn't have the funds for such a project, does it?"

At the time, the Soka Gakkai did not have a strong

financial base. It didn't even have enough community centers for the members to adequately carry out their activities.

Shin'ichi smiled and said to Mineko:"Don't worry. I'll earn it. I'll start writing book upon book and with the royalties, we'll build an internationally acclaimed school."

Hearing this, Mineko smiled back at her husband and nodded. The spring breeze rustled through the treetops and birds flew gaily overhead.

A month later, on May 3, 1960, Shin'ichi became the third president of the Soka Gakkai. Pressing duties awaited him, but amidst his heavy workload Shin'ichi arranged the purchase of the land in Kodaira and began carefully putting together a plan for establishing a school.

When he shared his intention with the top Soka Gakkai leaders, however, he was given a cold reception. "Starting a school is a major undertaking," they said. "The financial situation of the Soka Gakkai is very tight, and construction of temples and community centers is behind schedule. We simply don't have the funds to build a school."

The leaders' hands were full with the immediate challenges facing the organization, and they didn't have the mental energy to expend on founding a school. But Shin'ichi continued to take every opportunity to drive home the point to them that the establishment of a school based on humanism was indispensable to the realization of peace and happiness for humanity.

At the same time, while making plans to buy additional land in Kodaira, he also set about looking for land to purchase in Hachioji on which to build another school. An educational institution ranging from elementary through university level would require plenty of space. Shin'ichi officially announced his wish to establish a Soka University at the Seventh Student Division General Meeting on June 30, 1964, following the commemoration of the sixth anniversary of President Toda's death.

By this time, the Soka Gakkai had reached the membership target of three million member-households and had constructed and donated the Grand Reception Hall at the head temple, thereby achieving the goals that Shin'ichi had proposed when he became president. It was upon this solid foundation of kosen-rufu that Shin'ichi declared his new objective.

AFTER SHIN'ICHI announced the plan for building a Soka University at the student division meeting, the Soka Gakkai top leaders met on several occasions to decide on where the university would be built and when it would open. In the beginning of November 1965, a Soka University establishment steering committee was formed. President Yamamoto was named chairperson, while Soka Gakkai General Director Kiyoshi Jujo was appointed secretary. Thirty-five other committee members were selected from among Soka Gakkai vice general directors and members of the education and academic divisions.

The steering committee's inaugural meeting was held on November 26, 1965. Here, Shin'ichi proposed that first they aim to open a Soka High School in 1968, and then look to establishing the university sometime after 1970. He also mentioned that Hachioji was being considered as the site for the university, while the high school should be constructed on the land already purchased in Kodaira City.

He further stated that, while the general outline for the schools had until then been drafted by the Soka Gakkai executive officers, from now on the planning and implementation of the project would be left entirely to the steering committee. He then proposed the formation of three subcommittees: an establishment preparatory subcommittee, which would oversee the legal matters involved in establishing the academic institutions, as well as a Soka University subcommittee and a Soka High School subcommittee to specifically manage each separate enterprise. Shin'ichi's proposal was accepted, thus setting this momentous undertaking in motion.

However, this was the first time for any of the committee members to be involved in founding a school, and the fact was that they didn't know where to start. The high school subcommittee decided to begin by visiting and observing well-reputed high schools, boarding schools and schools known for their unique educational programs. They visited not only schools in Tokyo and the rest of the Kanto region but also those as far away as Gifu and Hyogo prefectures.

At their subcommittee meetings, members reported on such things as the curricula and facilities of the schools they visited, the numbers of students and faculty, tuition rates and school rules. They then carefully analyzed and discussed which elements might be adopted for the Soka High School. It was not rare for them to become so absorbed in deliberation that their meetings would go late into the night. Their passion was the driving force for the creation of the new school.

PREPARATIONS for the opening of Soka High School proceeded smoothly, and it was decided that a groundbreaking ceremony would be held on November 18, 1966. On April 10 of that year, Shin'ichi had visited the site in Kodaira City and discussed forthcoming plans with representative members of the steering committee.

As they walked around the wooded lot he had purchased six years earlier, Shin'ichi noticed that the land had been beautifully maintained. He remarked to Kiyoshi Jujo, the steering committee secretary: "I'm so touched. I can see that the Soka Gakkai members living in the area have been working hard."

Jujo and the other leaders blankly stared at Shin'ichi.

"You haven't noticed?" Shin'ichi asked. "Usually, when land like this is vacant people tend to use it as a garbage dump, but this whole area is clean and neat. I'm certain that the local members have been making a regular effort to keep it that way. Please look into it."

Jujo immediately contacted the local organization and discovered that in fact garbage and rubble had been dumped on the lot, and strong winds often blew litter into the trees, where it got caught. It pained the members in the neighborhood to see this, and so they took it upon themselves to clean up the site. They labored under the hot sun, fending off mosquitoes as they collected garbage and cleared weeds. In the six years since the land's purchase, they had cleaned it up more than a hundred times.

When Shin'ichi heard Jujo's report on this matter, he said with firm determination: "Having heard about the construction of Soka High School, many of our members have expressed a desire to make donations. Whether it is through contributing time or money, these ordinary men and women are eager to help build and protect our school. We need to ensure that, generation after generation, the students and teachers of Soka High School are always aware of the wonderful fact that from its very inception, their school has been supported by the sincere efforts of the people."

Through the dedicated endeavors of the Soka High School subcommittee members, the school's design was finished promptly. On August 2, the *Seikyo Shimbun* published an artist's rendition of what the campus would look like when it was completed. The planned school opened vistas of a new age and was a source of hope and inspiration for Soka Gakkai members throughout Japan.

IN OCTOBER, a month before the groundbreaking ceremony for Soka High School, a member of the high school subcommittee made a suggestion. Until that time, the plan had been to open a high school first, but after observing many different schools, it was clear that those institutions that jointly offered junior high and high school education produced far greater results. The subcommittee member therefore proposed that a Soka Junior High School be founded in tandem with the Soka High School.[3]

Adding a junior high school at this point in the process, however, would require changes in the campus design and other aspects of the planning, and the members of the steering committee expressed reservations about it. Many felt that they shouldn't bother altering an endeavor that was so smoothly proceeding.

But Shin'ichi Yamamoto supported the idea. He had in fact been concerned about the current situation of junior high school students—a situation in which high school entrance examinations weighed so heavily on them that they could not freely engage in either their studies or sports or other after-school activities. He said to the committee members: "Our ultimate goal is an all-inclusive educational system, which is why I am behind the idea of establishing a junior high school and high school together. I am also planning to have our university up and running in time for the first graduating high school class.

"In the future, I would like to establish an elementary school and a kindergarten, and I intend to build schools in places other than Tokyo as well."

Shin'ichi thought ahead to the twenty-first century as he spoke. "The value-creating education that President Makiguchi left to us is a great spiritual legacy of humanity. It is not just for the Japanese but for people the world over. I don't know when, but I am also determined to someday found a Soka University in the United States that will produce outstanding humanistic leaders dedicated to world peace. I regard education as my final undertaking."

Shin'ichi's vision was limitless.

In the end, the steering committee accepted the proposal to establish a junior high school together with the high school. This development was announced in the November 13 *Seikyo Shimbun*. Five days later, on November 18, 1966, the groundbreaking ceremony for the Soka Junior High School and Soka High School was held amid high spirits.

NOVEMBER 18 also marked the anniversary of President Makiguchi's death. Furthermore, it was the date in 1930 when the first volume of his *Soka Kyoikugaku Taikei* (The System of Value-Creating Education) was published, and subsequently designated as the date of the Soka Gakkai's founding.

It was a beautiful autumn day without a single cloud in the sky. Bathed in sunlight, the deep green foliage of the trees rustled in the gentle wind as if to give congratulations. Shin'ichi prayed earnestly that construction on the schools would reach a successful completion and open on schedule in April 1968. Since Josei Toda's death, he had keenly felt the need to establish a school that would implement President Makiguchi's value-creating education.

The shortcomings of the postwar Japanese educational system were evident on every front. Based on the principle of equal opportunity education, this democratic system adopted after World War II was highly effective in eliminating wealth and class discrimination. The enforcement of compulsory primary and junior high school education (six and three years, respectively) elevated the basic level of Japanese education, which resulted in an increase in the number of students advancing onto high school. By 1965, more than 70 percent of junior high graduates were continuing their education.

The unfortunate reality, however, was that although education had become much more widely available, it was not fulfilling its fundamental purpose of fostering individuals of humanity and character. Instead, there was a disproportionate emphasis on academic achievement. The competition for university entrance examinations was so stiff that many high school students came to regard their friends and schoolmates merely as adversaries in the struggle to receive a higher education.

At the same time, as Japanese society became more affluent, juvenile delinquency and crime dramatically increased. Society's overall tendency to pursue monetary wealth brought a deepening sense of moral decay. During this postwar period of remarkable economic growth, the goal of Japanese education became producing people who could further that trend.

As a result, economic growth was designated as the first and foremost priority of education on the whole, and the pursuit of such questions as the meaning of life, what is right and wrong, and what is genuine value were neglected. The outcome was a system of education that was devoid of a fundamental educational philosophy and had lost sight of its role in forging individual character.

WHENEVER SHIN'ICHI thought about what would happen if Japanese education were to continue on the haphazard course it was on and young people's spirits were to become increasingly impoverished, his heart grew heavy. He keenly felt the need for a system of education that taught the purpose of life and cultivated strong, enriched minds and genuine humanity. He thus made a personal vow that he would establish a school that implemented President Makiguchi's value-creating education as quickly as possible.

President Makiguchi conceptualized a system of pedagogy that aimed to foster talented individuals who could create value,[4] an activity that he defined as life's true purpose. He emphasized that the purpose of education was the happiness of children and enabling them to live happy lives as members of society. This was a revolutionary stance in an age focused on increasing national wealth and military power, and in which education was regarded as existing for the sake of the nation.

Makiguchi also believed that in order for people to be genuinely happy, it was essential that they work both for their own welfare as well as for that of others. In other words, the aim of education, he asserted, was to build a society in which the happiness of the individual equaled the prosperity of society as a whole. Defining a happy life as one in which value can be attained and actualized, he determined that the purpose of Soka education was to cultivate the individual's ability to create value, or to enhance individual character.

In the ensuing volumes of *Soka Kyoikugaku Taikei* (The System of Value-Creating Education), Makiguchi offered a number of concrete proposals for educational reform and new educational methods, such as the half-day school system.[5] Makiguchi's pedagogy was developed during his more than thirty-year career as an educator and proven through his hands-on experience. It was a unique educational theory that distinguished itself from the abstract, conceptual educational theories of the day, lacking as they did efficacy in the actual teaching arena.

We now live in a different age and today there may be aspects of Makiguchi's proposed reforms that cannot be applied without adaptation, but his basic theories outline a humanistic education that offers illuminating prospects for the future.

Three leading Japanese intellectuals of the time contributed prefaces to the first volume of *The System of Value-Creating Education*. Inazo Nitobe,[6] who had served as undersecretary of the League of Nations, praised the work in his preface, calling it "a masterpiece long-awaited by contemporary Japan."

THE SCHOLAR of Japanese folklore and contemporary of Makiguichi, Kunio Yanagida, also lauded *The System of Value-Creating Education,* stating: "I recommend this work without hesitation, for I believe that it offers original values that are not found elsewhere and can thus break through the impasse faced by the world of education today."

And Suketoshi Tanabe, a sociologist specializing in French studies, wrote in his preface: "In a word, this work, with its solid theoretical foundation and based on long years of practical experience, introduces precisely the education that is most needed by Japan today."

He also remarked: "The French elementary school principal [Jean-Henri] Fabre was an educator whose life was devoted to the study of insects. When he wrote his *Souvenirs entomologiques* (Entomological Souvenirs), he was regarded as the pride of France, a land of learning. In fact, the French education minister visited him on behalf of the country and personally expressed his appreciation.

The elementary school principal Tsunesaburo Maki-guchi spent his life struggling against every sort of perse-cution and hardship, expending every ounce of his energy until finally he composed his epochal *The System of Value-Creating Education*. How will Japan, a land of cul-ture, reward this great educator, who is the pride of the nation?"

In reality, however, Japan's military government, which had adopted State Shinto and led the nation into war, imprisoned Makiguchi, a man who carried aloft the ban-ner of the correct teaching of Buddhism and dedicated his life to the happiness and peace of humanity. He died in prison on November 18, 1944—exactly fourteen years after the publication of the first of his four-volume *The System of Value-Creating Education*.

Militarist Japan labeled this great educator and Bud-dhist leader a traitor and rewarded him with death in prison. This act has left a dark stain on the history of Japan that will never disappear.

As third president of the Soka Gakkai, Shin'ichi Yamamoto regarded the establishment of the Soka Junior High School and Soka High School as his personal struggle in order to widely communicate the correctness of his predecessor, Tsunesaburo Makiguchi, and to prove the veracity of his educational philosophy. Shin'ichi also regarded it as the initial step in his grand vision of realizing world peace.

Construction began not long after the groundbreaking ceremony, and the sound of jackhammers working on this hope-filled project resounded in Musashino. In March of the following year, 1967, an application was submitted to the Tokyo metropolitan government for legal recognition of the Soka School Corporation, and in April for the establishment of the Soka Junior High School and Soka High School.

THE APPLICATION to the Tokyo metropolitan government for corporate status cited the educational goals of the Soka school system articulated by Shin'ichi Yamamoto: "fostering people of great talent" and "fostering rich humanity combined with practical ability."

"Fostering people of great talent" distinguished value-creating education from that focused on producing mere intellectuals without experience in the real world. It was also innately different from educational systems aimed exclusively at sending students to famous universities or that catered to children with high IQs. Rather, it would provide students with mental and physical training while drawing forth and nurturing their highest potential and supplying them with the confidence to become future leaders of society.

"Fostering rich humanity combined with practical ability" referred to students acquiring the practical abilities necessary to be leaders of society while simultaneously developing a boundless humanity based on the ideal of respect for the dignity of life.

From the time that the applications were submitted, the effort to establish a school system that promoted a new humanistic and all-encompassing education gained momentum. In spring of that year, 1967, the school emblem, flag and uniforms were decided on. The emblem was a stylized design of a pen flanked on each side by phoenix feathers.

Two uniforms were chosen, one for commuting to and from school and to wear on special occasions, and one to wear while on campus. The uniform for commuting was a dark navy blue jacket and slacks with black trim. The jacket had a standing collar and was fastened with hooks. The on-campus uniform was designed to be more relaxed and comfortable—a cardigan-style jacket in navy with white trim and white sweatpants.

The school colors were designated as blue, yellow and red, symbolizing respectively, wisdom, glory and passion—the school's mottoes.

Though the design of the school had to be changed to accommodate the addition of the junior high school—for example, adding a fourth story to the main classroom buildings—the project moved forward on schedule.

Construction is hope, and Shin'ichi was filled with anticipation at the prospect of the completed campus.

In May, Shin'ichi visited the construction site. He wanted to see the progress for himself and to thank the workers for their efforts. Then, on June 19, the Tokyo metropolitan government approved the applications for the legal recognition of the Soka School Corporation as well as the establishment of the Soka Junior High School and Soka High School, accelerating the momentum for the schools' opening.

O N JULY 14, 1967, an article announcing guide-lines for prospective applicants to the Soka Junior High School and Soka High School appeared at last in the *Seikyo Shimbun*. Young people preparing to enter junior high school or high school the following year, as well as their parents and families, and, indeed, all Soka Gakkai members, read the announcement with great excitement.

The junior high school would enroll two hundred students for its first class, while the high school would enroll three hundred. Youth who had been hoping to enter one of the two schools ever since they learned of their establishment began studying in earnest for the entrance examinations. At the same time, pamphlets providing information about the schools and the application process were produced and distributed widely in an effort to further attract applicants.

The Soka High School subcommittee, meanwhile, had been busy interviewing candidates for teaching positions at the school since before the groundbreaking ceremony, and now it had reached the final stages of the selection process.

The most important factor in students' learning environment is neither a school's buildings nor its natural setting. It is the teachers. That was why the subcommittee members put special effort into selecting the faculty.

Shin'ichi Yamamoto repeatedly urged them: "It's important to have a fine campus, but more important is that you do your utmost to hire fine teachers. I also hope that you will make valuing the faculty the tradition of the Soka schools. Education ultimately comes down to educators."

By the end of December that year, twenty-four teachers had been hired. The following year, 1968, would see the schools' opening.

On January 6, Shin'ichi held a meeting with representatives of the schools' faculty and staff over dinner. He said to them: "The Soka schools will soon enter their initial stage of development. In any endeavor, building a foundation requires incredible effort and is extremely challenging. At the same time, however, it is the most important task. If you do your best now, you will be able to build a solid and indestructible foundation for the schools' future growth. The schools will flourish to the extent that you work hard. And further, your efforts will polish your lives as teachers and as human beings.

"I am certain that all your struggles now will become golden memories that you can be proud of throughout your lives."

SHIN'ICHI SPOKE earnestly: "The things we learn through our struggles become our greatest treasures. Many young and talented teachers will follow in your footsteps. What matters is the wisdom you impart to them when they appear. If you don't give your all now and create your own record of achievement, you cannot offer them any inspiration.

"Now is the time to stand up with passion. The wellspring of education is your enthusiasm as educators and as human beings. Let's work together to make the best school in Japan! Let's build an unparalleled institution of humanistic education for the sake of the twenty-first century. You are the pioneers in this effort. I hope each of you will think of yourself as the schools' founder."

Engraving these words in their hearts, the faculty and staff strove energetically to build the schools' foundation.

Applications for enrollment to the junior high school were accepted from January 19, and for the high school, from February 1. On January 29, the schools' were completed and the opening ceremony was held. Shin'ichi attended the ceremony, arriving early to inspect the auditorium, gymnasium and other facilities beforehand. The gymnasium contained two basketball courts and there were practice areas for judo and kendo on the basement level. Adjacent to the gymnasium was an eighty-two-foot pool and tennis and volleyball courts.

The school was equipped with all the latest facilities, including a language lab and a biology lab with television cameras and receivers. The schools' focus on cultivating rich humanity in their students was also evident in the arts education facilities, which boasted a professional art studio and a music room with its own small stage.

As Shin'ichi strolled around the campus viewing the school buildings, he was happy to see that the final product was exactly what he had imagined; it was the perfect setting for nurturing young phoenixes who would take flight into the twenty-first century. *President Makiguchi and President Toda would be overjoyed*, he thought, powerful emotion rising in his heart.

AFTER THE OPENING ceremony, Shin'ichi planted a gingko sapling in front of the gymnasium to commemorate the occasion. As he looked up into the sky, he thought: *Now all we need are the students. I wonder what these young people who share my ideals will be like. Everything depends on them.*

The period for accepting applications to the junior high school ended on January 30. Nearly eight hundred students had applied for the two hundred openings. The junior high school entrance examination was held on February 1, and the results were announced on the 5th. In the end, 220 students were accepted, eighty-six from Tokyo and the remaining 134 from other regions of Japan.

Applications for the high school, on the other hand, were accepted from February 1 through 13. Nearly fifteen hundred students applied for the three hundred places. The high school entrance exam was held on February 15, a day that saw the heaviest snowfall in Tokyo in seventeen years. By nightfall, several modes of public transportation had ground to a halt and the expressways and roads were closed. Shin'ichi chanted every moment he could for the students who had come from all over Japan, praying for them to successfully complete their examinations and safely return home.

On February 19, the examination results were announced: 332 students were accepted, 179 from Tokyo and 153 from other regions. Surpassing all expectations, nearly 250 of the new students to both schools were from areas out of reasonable commuting distance. The school dormitory could only accommodate 170 students, so lodging had to be found close to the campus for some eighty students.

When Shin'ichi heard this from Soka schools General Director Kazumasa Morikawa and Principal Takashi Oyamada, he said: "We have six weeks until the entrance ceremony; that's not much time. We need to work together to find lodging for all the students. I'll look, too.

"If we don't find lodging for everyone quickly, the students' families are sure to worry, and it would be terrible for the students. Our job is to make sure that the students who are coming here with great expectations can throw themselves confidently into their studies."

THE SEARCH for student lodgings began. For his part, Shin'ichi spoke to Soka Gakkai leaders living near the school. School faculty members also worked in concert under the leadership of the head of the physical education department, Michiya Komori.

They knocked on the doors of homes that were already renting rooms to students or that appeared to have extra rooms and asked if they would be willing to provide lodging to students of the Soka schools coming from other parts of Japan. Few families, however, were willing to do so. Some had prejudiced or mistaken views of the Soka Gakkai, and when they heard the words "Soka schools" they immediately refused.

Others asked if the Soka schools were a place to train

future Soka Gakkai leaders. When that happened, the faculty members took it as a good opportunity to change preconceived opinions, patiently explaining the purpose of the schools' establishment and their educational aims. In some cases, they visited the same home repeatedly, doing their utmost to persuade the potential landlord. In this manner, they eventually found the necessary accommodations, one hard-won room at a time.

These students are leaving the care of their parents and coming all the way to Tokyo to study at our school. We simply can't allow them to worry about where they're going to stay. This was the thought foremost on the teachers' minds. And so by early March, they had succeeded in finding housing for all the students.

April 8, the long-anticipated day of the entrance ceremony, finally arrived. After the ceremony was completed, the new students and their parents gathered in the circular driveway in front of the campus main entrance, where they waited to greet the schools' founder, Shin'-ichi Yamamoto. Many of them were meeting him for the first time, and they were all very excited.

When Shin'ichi's car arrived at 11:50 AM, everyone cheered and applauded. He stepped out of the car and greeted them with a slight bow. As he shook hands with the rows of students, he said in a cheerful voice: "Congratulations! You're all setting out on a new journey today. Do your best!"

The students' responses echoed into the air.

AFTER SHIN'ICHI YAMAMOTO arrived at the campus, a ceremony was held to unveil a monument inscribed with the school motto. The monument stood on an island planted with trees in the middle of the circular driveway just inside the campus main gate.

Representing the Soka Gakkai future division, Shin'-ichi's third son Hirotaka, who was in the fourth grade of elementary school, pulled the cord releasing the cloth covering the monument. In addition to Hirotaka, Shin'-ichi brought his wife, Mineko, and their eldest son, Masahiro, to the event that day. He wanted to firmly establish in his family the spirit to protect the schools for the sake of future world peace.

The red-and-white cloth fell to the ground, revealing the monument. It was a slab of black granite ten feet wide and 3.3 feet high inscribed in Shin'ichi's calligraphy with the Chinese characters for the school motto, "Wisdom, Glory, Passion."

Principal Takashi Oyamada then requested that Shin'-ichi hear the students perform the school song. Sitting in a chair prepared for him in front of the monument, Shin'ichi listened to their energetic voices: "Day breaks on the vast open field . . ."

The students stood proudly, their faces flushed with emotion as they sang with their whole beings in an expression of their determination. Shin'ichi looked at each of them and spoke to them in his heart: *Thank you. Welcome to the school I founded. I will devote my life to opening the way for you.*

When they finished, he said: "Your singing was wonderful. It overflowed with hope and limitless dreams for the future. Let's take a photograph together to celebrate today's entrance ceremony as a fresh departure in your lives."

The students cheered. Shin'ichi then pointed to the bridge next to the gymnasium and said: "Before the photograph, I'd like to go onto that bridge with you. There's a wonderful view from it." The bridge spanned the Tamagawa Aqueduct.

The high school students stayed behind and prepared for their photo with Shin'ichi while the junior high school students followed him to the bridge, the stairway to which had a ceremonial ribbon hanging across it. Announcing that they would conduct a ribbon-cutting ceremony to open the bridge officially, Principal Oyamada asked Shin'ichi to do the honors. The students applauded as Shin'ichi complied.

"All right, let's walk on it!" Shin'ichi called out, and they climbed the stairs to the top of the bridge. From there, they could see the woods of Musashino and distant mountains, beyond which Mount Fuji rose majestically in an image of hope.

SHIN'ICHI SAID to the junior high school students standing around him: "I have named this Glory Bridge." He had been requested to give the structure a name by some of the committee members working on the schools' opening when he visited the campus to observe the progress of the construction. The name represented his expectations that the students would develop into capable people who would realize a glorious future for humanity.

Shin'ichi continued: "Please look at the scenery. Your school is surrounded by mountains, rivers, the Musashino plain and green trees. Mountains symbolize champions, while rivers represent purity of spirit. The vast Musashino plain signifies your boundless dreams and the greenery, a rich spiritual life. I hope that each time you cross Glory Bridge you will confirm to yourselves that you are leading a life of glory, and that you will always do your best and never be defeated, no matter what happens."

The Soka schools were being built from scratch, and Shin'ichi wished to assign a clear significance to everything, including this single bridge, as a way of creating a proud school tradition. The students nodded in understanding as they listened to him speak, their eyes shining with hope.

There had been a twenty-eight-year gap between the ages of Tsunesaburo Makiguchi and Josei Toda, and between Toda and Shin'ichi. Now forty years old, Shin'-ichi was about twenty-eight years older than the students he was speaking to. He was filled with emotion to think that these first-year students, with whom he shared the same age difference as he did with his mentor, would inherit his vision of world peace.

Looking at history, Plato was also said to have been about forty years old when he established his Academy to carry on the teachings of his mentor, Socrates. Realizing that he was embarking on the final undertaking of his life—education—together with the first classes of the Soka schools, a strong fighting spirit welled up from within Shin'ichi's life.

He said: "Let's give three cheers: one for your glorious futures, one for the completion of this Glory Bridge and one for the first entrance ceremony of the Soka schools!"

Principal Oyamada led the cheers, and the youthful, spirited voices of the students rang out through the sky over Musashino.

SHIN'ICHI THEN TOOK photos with the students in several groups on the stairs of Glory Bridge. Looking at them lined up on the bridge, Shin'ichi said: "You're all very tall."

A voice immediately burst out from among the boys: "Actually, we're normal height. You're short!"

Flustered by this, Vice Principal Fumitaka Morotani shot the pupil a threatening glance, but at that moment everyone including Shin'ichi burst out laughing, which put both the students and their parents standing nearby at ease.

Shin'ichi then suggested that he also take a photo with the parents, to whom he joked: "Your children are all so wonderful. Some might be rude and say that you couldn't possibly be their parents, but I would never think such a thing!" The parents heartily laughed.

He then remarked in all seriousness: "Thank you very much for sending your precious children to the Soka schools. I promise I will take good care of them. Please look forward to their growth and don't worry about anything. I promise you that in a year you will be astonished at their progress."

It was then time for lunch. The students enjoyed a traditional celebratory meal with red beans and rice in the school cafeteria. In the afternoon, Shin'ichi participated in an unveiling ceremony for a sculpture titled "Youth and Eagle" next to the gymnasium. He had personally donated the thirteen-foot bronze piece to the school. When the red-and-white cloth was pulled off, the image of an eagle on a rock with its wings outstretched and a youth below was revealed. It was a powerful work.

Shin'ichi explained to the students who gazed at it curiously: "To me, this eagle represents passion and the young man represents wisdom. Eagles are strong and they can fly long distances. They are monarchs of the sky. I hope that all of you will be as strong and bold as an eagle. I also hope you will hone your intellect and fly with solid conviction toward your ideals, devoting yourself to working for peace in Japan and the entire world."

SHIN'ICHI YAMAMOTO'S voice grew stronger: "The most important thing in your youth is to challenge yourself and not be held back or defeated by your own weaknesses. Please don't forget that self-control and winning over yourself are the key to all victory."

Shin'ichi spoke passionately, determined to convey the true path of life to these pure-hearted young people. He then said to Principal Oyamada: "Let's go see the dormitory. I want to encourage the students who will be living there away from their parents."

The residence hall was named Glory Dormitory and was located adjacent to the school's athletic field near Takanodai Station on the Seibu Kokubunji Line. A total of 162 students—eighty-five from the junior high school and seventy-seven from the high school—lodged there. They were from all over Japan, including as far south as the Amami Oshima Islands and as far north as Hokkaido's Shiretoko Peninsula.

The chief dorm supervisor was Yasuo Nagamine, head of the Japanese language department. He had graduated from the Tokyo University of Education and taught at a prefectural high school in Kumamoto Prefecture. In his mid-thirties, he was a kindhearted man of small stature, with thick brows and a handsome face.

Nagamine gave Shin'ichi a tour of the hall, showing him the rooms and other facilities. Shin'ichi said to the teachers who were serving as dorm supervisors: "A dormitory is an extremely important environment in which students can forge their character and build friendships. I know you are busy with your various responsibilities, but I hope you will remember that all of our students are like my own beloved children. Please look after them on my behalf, both in their daily lives and their studies."

Shin'ichi then spoke with ten student representatives in one of the dormitory rooms. Smiling, he said to the youths, some of whom looked shy and nervous: "In England there are a number of famous private educational institutions such as Eaton and Rugby that have produced many of their nation's greatest leaders. Known as 'public schools,' they use the dormitory system. In other words, living in a dorm is one way to develop yourselves."

SHIN'ICHI CONTINUED: "You may feel lonely at first living in a dormitory away from home, but it can also be a very meaningful experience for you. You may also feel restricted by all the rules and regulations, but dorm life can lead you to acquire self-discipline, become independent and foster deep friendships.

"Unlike the tradition-rich dormitories of England's well-known public schools, the history of the Soka schools' dormitory has just begun. I hope that you will look at yourselves as pioneers and contribute to our schools' establishing their own proud traditions. Please support each other in making this Glory Dormitory the best in all Japan and the world.

"The first step is for everyone to get on well together, older students looking after the younger students, and younger students respecting their older counterparts. Things may be difficult at times, but in the future you will look back on these three or six years as a wonderful memory. Whatever happens, please hang in there and do your best."

Shin'ichi gazed at each of their faces. Some of them appeared so childlike and innocent with their closely cropped heads. Learning of the Soka schools' establishment, they had left their hometowns and gathered from across Japan filled with hope and determination. Thinking of this, Shin'ichi wanted to warmly embrace all of them.

With deep affection, he said: "From now on, I'll look after you like a parent. You are my precious children." The students beamed with joy.

On this day, a new door of history opened and the Soka schools set forth on a path of development in high hopes. For Shin'ichi Yamamoto, it marked the true beginning of his ascent up the mountain of his life's final undertaking—education. From that point on, the Soka schools were never out of Shin'ichi's thoughts, and he continued to regularly encourage the students in one form or another.

ON THE EIGHTH of every month, to commemorate the day the Soka schools' entrance ceremony had been held, Shin'ichi sent snacks to the dormitory. He wanted to remind the students of their determination on that first day and to encourage them to keep doing their best.

On June 14, more than two months after the entrance ceremony, Shin'ichi attended the opening of the schools' tennis courts. On Sunday, June 30, he went again for the opening of the swimming pool. Teachers and representatives of the student body participated in this latter event.

Wearing a polo shirt, Shin'ichi cut the ceremonial ribbon and officially opened the pool. He spent time mingling with the students by the poolside, and when it came time for the swimming race, he fired the signal gun. The blue surface of the pool awoke with silver waves as the students dove in to the cheers of their friends. "Do your best!" Shin'ichi called as he watched the swimmers glide through the water.

He later went to the tennis courts and played an energetic game of tennis with the junior high school students. He wanted to create fond memories with them. Hoping to get to know them, he spoke to them as they played, etching their faces, names and hometowns in his mind. Knowing a person's face and name is indeed the first step in creating and deepening bonds of friendship.

Shin'ichi also played ping-pong with students in the gymnasium, piling up points with his quick moves. Whenever he smashed the ball, the students applauded. "I'm pretty good, aren't I?" he said. They all expressed their agreement. "I hope that all of you will find something that you like and excel at, like a subject in school or a sport. That is how you build self-confidence. If you can succeed in one endeavor, you learn that through effort you can succeed in others. Developing our skills requires practice."

Shin'ichi also took a photograph to commemorate the day with students in front of the sculpture "Youth and Eagle."

AFTER THE PHOTOGRAPH was taken, one of the students summoned up his courage and said in a determined voice: "Sensei, please come back with us to the dormitory!" The youth's name was Yasuyuki Tadokoro. He was a high school student from Fukuoka Prefecture and was the head of the dormitory students' executive committee. From the time when Shin'ichi had visited the residence hall on the day of the entrance ceremony and talked with the small group of students, Tadokoro had cherished the hope that he would come again and meet with all the students.

Shin'ichi understood Tadokoro's feelings well, and he was glad to see that the young man was so considerate of his fellow dormitory students.

"I don't have time today," Shin'ichi said, "but I will visit the dorm the next time I come here, I promise. We'll always be together during your three or six years at the Soka schools, and even after you've graduated. There's no need to worry. We'll have plenty of chances to get together."

Hearing Shin'ichi's words, the students felt the deep bond they had with their schools' founder.

Shin'ichi then climbed the stairs up to Glory Bridge with the students and teachers who were with him. Principal Oyamada pointed to a vacant piece of land on the other side of the bridge that was once a tea plantation and still had some tea bushes growing on it, saying: "We are planning to make that area into our athletic field by next year."

"Next year?" Shin'ichi asked. "Would it be possible, for the students' sake, to move the preparation forward so that it will be ready by the start of the second term?"

"Perhaps," the principal replied.

"Please see what you can do," Shin'ichi said. "The wellspring of humanistic education is constantly thinking about how to help students to do their best—joyfully, cheerfully and brimming with hope. Everyone seemed to really enjoy themselves today, so I think it's a good idea to put on a school festival or some such event from time to time.

"It's especially important to provide opportunities for the dorm students and those students lodging off campus to create happy school memories. What would you think about having a special festival for all boarding students before everyone returns home for the summer break?"

"That's a wonderful idea," Principal Oyamada agreed.

"Well then," Shin'ichi remarked, "since I have your approval, may I announce it to the students?"

"By all means," the principal replied.

Shin'ichi then turned to the students and said: "I just spoke with your principal about this. I know you are busy with your studies every day, so at the end of this term we're going to hold a special school festival for you."

The students cheered.

SHIN'ICHI YAMAMOTO waited for the students' cheers to subside, then continued speaking: "Let's have everyone write a letter home on the day of the festival. I'd like even those of you who don't usually write letters to do so. Your parents will be relieved to hear from you. It's a way to show them your appreciation.

"Also, the land over there across the bridge will be made into an athletic field by the start of the second term. When it's finished, we'll have two playing fields—the one in front of the dormitory and that one. I'll come and visit you when the new athletic field is ready. Let's meet again then."

In accord with Shin'ichi's suggestion, on the night of July 14, the day after the first-term examinations were finished, a bonfire festival called "Glory Festival" was held on the playing field in front of the dormitory. In the afternoon, as part of the festivities, Shin'ichi invited all the boarding students to a special film presentation at the Soka Culture Center in Shinano-machi.

It was the first time in a while for many of the students to see a movie. When it was finished, Shin'ichi presented them with various small gifts, including cans of juice, towels and erasers. They then returned happily to the school where the main event of the day, the bonfire, was held in the evening. When the stack of logs was lit, the flames leapt high into the night sky with a great roar. It was a night of song, dance, skits and a costume parade.

Both the principal and the chief dormitory supervisor also performed. Though their movements were unpolished, they were eager to do anything to please the students—a spirit that was fast becoming a tradition among the teachers at the Soka schools. The awkward dance of the scholarly Principal Oyamada won roars of laughter from the students.

A little more than three months had passed since classes had started, and some students had become very homesick, crying themselves to sleep at night. Fights had broken out among some students as well. But now, as they stood around the bonfire with their arms around each other's shoulders singing their hearts out, they were all friends. They felt joy and pride to be young and students of the Soka schools.

The athletic field on the far side of the Tamagawa Aqueduct across Glory Bridge was completed at the end of summer vacation.

THE CEREMONY and festival opening the new athletic field was held on September 6. Shin'ichi Yamamoto had caught a cold, and he was burning up with a fever. However, knowing that the students had been preparing for the event and how much they were looking forward to seeing him, Shin'ichi was determined to attend at any cost. He had his doctor give him an injection for his fever and headed for the Soka schools.

Before the ceremony, he stopped by Glory Dormitory to fulfill the promise he had made back in June to the dorm students on the day the swimming pool was opened. He spoke with the students there, carefully observing each of them. If he noticed that they looked even a little tired or under the weather, he warmly asked after their health and if they were getting enough sleep.

The principal and others then showed Shin'ichi the

dormitory's study hall and other facilities before heading down to the athletic field for the opening ceremony at half past three. They crossed Glory Bridge and came upon an arch decorated with the English word *Congratulations* that had been set up on the other side. Shin'ichi cut the celebratory ribbon affixed to the arch and officially opened the field. At that moment, the Brass Band on the bridge struck up a fanfare and a confetti ball was released, raining down balloons and confetti.

The festival marking the opening of the new athletic field thus began. The first part consisted of various team competitions, including a mock cavalry battle, in which a student stood upon the linked arms of three other students and tried to collect the headbands of the opposing teams. They also played a pole-toppling game in which each team attempted to bring down the other team's pole.

Shin'ichi fired the starting gun and the students energetically started to play. Even while he watched the games, Shin'ichi spoke with the boarding students who had come from Okinawa and other distant parts of Japan, continuing his efforts to get to know them.

Having heard that a certain junior high school student had lost his father in a coalmining accident that summer, he immediately arranged to talk to him. "I know it must be very hard for you," Shin'ichi said to the boy, "but please don't be defeated. I will be here for you like a father, so please don't worry and give your best to your studies. I'll ask the principal to look after you, and if you have any problems, just speak to him and he'll get in touch with me."

Shin'ichi gave his all to encouraging each person he met. For him, every moment was a win-or-lose struggle.

AFTER THE GAMES, there was a performance by the Brass Band. Then a large stack of wood in the center of the athletic field was ignited for a bonfire and the second part of the festival began. Some of the students performed songs, while others performed skits satirizing contradictions of modern society and humorously depicting school life and their teachers and fellow students. Between the skits several students read poems that conveyed their determinations for the twenty-first century.

The finale was a choral rendition of the school's dormitory song. Everyone sang together:

> The greenery flourishes
> In the fields of Musashino
> And its flowers are fragrant.
> For what purpose
> Do we young phoenixes cultivate wisdom?
> To shoulder the next generation.
> Let us boldly take flight into the future.

As the students sang, their faces shone with strong resolve.

It was a solemn melody. Shin'ichi leaned forward and listened to the song with his whole being. The dormitory students had composed the lyrics themselves, having begun work on them in late April. This endeavor was the result of a suggestion made by chief dorm supervisor

Yasuo Nagamine, who wanted to encourage the students to take pride in their dormitory.

Nagamine first had to explain to them what a dormitory song was. He said: "In Japan's old-system high schools,[7] every dormitory had a song. For example, such prestigious institutions as the First Higher School and the Third Higher School, which later merged respectively with the University of Tokyo's faculty of general education and Kyoto University, both had famous dormitory songs. All these songs were filled with the students' determination to shoulder the future of their society and their nation. I'd like to propose that you compose your own dormitory song that conveys your resolve to grow up into world leaders. What do you think?"

The boarding students embraced the idea wholeheartedly.

"Great! Let's do it then! Let's make the best dormitory song of all! Please submit your lyric ideas to me and we'll put them all together," Nagamine said.

VERY FEW of the students had any experience writing song lyrics, however. For inspiration, they listened to the dormitory songs of old and paged through poetry collections. They then wrote and submitted their own ideas to Nagamine. In the end, Nagamine received some sixty submissions. He formed a committee to go through them, and they found all of the lyrics to be quite good.

But there was one that stood out above the rest. Composed by a student from Osaka named Yuya Okura, the song had four stanzas in total and began with the lines: *The greenery flourishes / In the fields of Musashino.* Each stanza started by describing one of the four seasons of Musashino, followed by a question concerning the reasons students spend their youth at the Soka schools, and then its answer.

The first stanza asked, *For what purpose do we young phoenixes cultivate wisdom?* and answered, *To shoulder the next generation.* The second asked, *For what purpose do we young phoenixes burn with passion?* and answered, *To build a prosperous society.* The third asked, *For what purpose do we young phoenixes love the people?* and answered, *To bring the people happiness.* And the final stanza asked, *For what purpose do we young phoenixes seek a glorious future?* and answered, *To construct a world of peace.*

It was a song fused with tremendous spirit that inquired about life's purpose, reaffirmed lofty goals and conveyed firm resolve to advance toward them.

Yuya Okura's grandmother and older brother were both very active Soka Gakkai members, and Yuya himself frequently read the *Seikyo Shimbun*. Seeing the announcement of the opening of the Soka schools and a photograph of them in the paper, he decided that he wanted to study there and take the entrance examination. But having never lived away from home, he became very homesick once he was actually there. He felt lonely, and found his classes difficult.

Amid these circumstances, he questioned his reasons for choosing to attend Soka High School and what was the purpose of his studies. Looking for answers to these questions, he pored over guidance by Shin'ichi

Yamamoto, the school's founder, which he found in the *Seikyo Shimbun* and other writings. He then wove the conclusions he reached into lyrics for the dormitory song. For him, the song represented the culmination of the intellectual quest of his youth.

The lyrics committee unanimously backed Okura's submission. It was then decided that Yasuyuki Sugita, a music teacher at the school, would be asked to compose the music for the song.

IN MID-JUNE, when Nagamine made his request, Sugita immediately set to work writing the music for the dormitory song. Thinking of the students, young phoenixes boldly taking flight into the skies of the twenty-first century, he began to compose a bright and dignified song along the lines of "Song of Worldwide Kosen-rufu."

When the song was completed, Sugita played it for the students on the piano and asked them what they thought. Contrary to his expectations, however, they weren't satisfied. They said it wasn't stirring enough, and that they would prefer something similar to the melodies of the old prewar dormitory songs. Sugita realized that the students were looking for a more traditional-sounding song, one that conveyed lofty ideals and that they could sing when they were alone and feel inspired.

He tried once more, throwing himself energetically into the task. When he was finished, he taped himself playing it on the piano and took it to the dorm.

"I think I've composed just the kind of song you're looking for," he said to the students.

This time they loved it.

"This is what we wanted!" "It's just as we had imagined!" They were overjoyed. Thus, the Soka schools dormitory song was created.

At the first Glory Festival on July 14, the students sang the song in chorus. They also made a recording of it, which they sent along with the lyrics to Shin'ichi.

Listening to the song with his wife, Mineko, Shin'ichi remarked: "It's very good, isn't it? It's refreshing and powerful and it brims with the students' spirit as they prepare for their advance into the next century. They've created a real masterpiece."

He played the tape every day, thinking about the students' futures and praying for their growth.

At the annual summer training course held in August at the head temple that year, Soka High School students who were attending the course as members of the high school division sang the dormitory song for Shin'ichi. As he and the other participants listened, Shin'ichi said to a youth division leader sitting nearby: "It's a wonderful song, don't you think? One of the students wrote the lyrics. I really like it."

AS SHIN'ICHI YAMAMOTO listened to the high school division members singing the Soka schools dormitory song, he felt the desire to respond in some way to their innovative spirit. He thus decided to compose a fifth stanza for them.

The annual summer training course ended on August 23. As the central figure of the course, Shin'ichi was extremely busy, but he still managed to find time to compose the additional stanza. After deeply pondering the first four, he concluded that "friendship" should be the theme of the fifth.

When he picked up his pen, words came rushing forth. He went over them carefully again and again, polishing them until he was felt the stanza was complete:

> *We can see Mount Fuji from Musashino*
> *Where pure streams flow.*
> *For what purpose*
> *Do we young phoenixes work for peace?*
> *To open a path for wonderful friends.*
> *You and I, together,*
> *Let us take flight into the future.*

The line, *To open a path for wonderful friends*, expressed Shin'ichi's own determination to devote his life to paving the way for the Soka schools students.

The news that Shin'ichi had written a fifth stanza for the dormitory song was announced to the students on Monday, September 2, at the ceremony for the start of the new term. Hearing this, the students cheered with joy. It was then decided that the entire student body would perform the song with the new stanza for Shin'-ichi at the opening of the new athletic field that would take place on September 6.

The bonfire crackled as it burned. The students sang with their whole beings, their faces glowing even brighter than the flames. Their voices became more forceful when they came to the fifth stanza:

> *To open a path for wonderful friends.*
> *You and I, together,*
> *Let us take flight into the future.*

The students found dual meaning in the phrase *You and I, together.* One was that "you" meant their friends, while "I" referred to themselves. And the other was that "you" referred to themselves and "I" was Shin'ichi Yama-moto, their schools' founder. As they sang, the students felt extremely close to Shin'ichi, as if they were engaged in a joint struggle of parent and child advancing together toward the future.

WHEN the students finished singing, Shin'ichi asked them to come forward and sit in front of him. In an exuberant voice, he said to them: "I have participated in many meetings, but none have been as refreshing and touching as this."

He then told them of his plans to open a junior high school and high school for girls, as well as a women's college, and reaffirmed his belief that the Soka Junior High School and Soka High School were the starting point and the axis of all these educational projects. He remarked: "A philosopher has said, 'The further the source, the longer the stream.' You are the source and the foundation of these endeavors. There are little more than five hundred of you, and as such you are a small source. But if a source is great, then its stream will flow eternally.

"As the founder of your schools, I will never forget you as long as I live. You are all in my heart. I am convinced that outstanding leaders dedicated to world peace will emerge from among you. In the past, the students of the old-system high schools who sang dormitory songs went on to become the leaders of Japanese society. I believe that those who sing this dormitory song will be the leaders of the next generation, the leaders of the twenty-first century. I am certain that the day will come when it is loved by people throughout Japan and the world."

And in fact, years later, it would become the official school song of the Soka Junior High School and Soka High School.

Shin'ichi concluded his remarks to the promising youth sitting before him as if infusing them with his spirit: "I care for you all very much. I will give my entire life to working on your behalf. That is my fundamental resolve. I would like to close my talk today with the wish that you will take good care of your health, forge your capability and distinguish yourselves as talented individuals of rich humanity and practical ability."

Tears shone in the eyes of the students as they looked intently at their schools' founder. Some of them pressed their lips together in firm determination. It was a dramatic life-to-life exchange between mentor and disciple in the spirit of parent and child, individuals dedicated to the struggle for peace and justice.

TOWARD THE END of the first term, the faculty of the Soka schools began to discuss the issue of how to provide suitable guidance for the students lodging off campus. The teachers couldn't sufficiently supervise these students, who had considerably more freedom than their counterparts living in the dormitory and, accordingly, more temptations. For example, some of them were frequently invited to join in mah-jongg parties by university students rooming in the same homes.

The faculty were seriously concerned about this issue, but they knew that simply forbidding the students to do this or that would not solve the problem. The important thing was for each of the off-campus lodgers to reconfirm his awareness as a Soka schools student and become strong enough to discipline himself. The faculty thus decided to establish an off-campus student organization so that these students could support and encourage each other on a daily basis.

When Shin'ichi Yamamoto heard about this decision, he heartily agreed. "That's very important," he said. "I believe that the fundamental purpose of education is to foster personal autonomy in people. Having the students think for themselves and confer with each other and enabling them to find a way to regulate themselves is true education."

With the hope that these students would experience their youth as a glorious time in their lives, Shin'ichi named the new off-campus student organization Glory Group. When the students learned of this, they were filled with a fresh sense of pride.

On September 15, a gathering was held in the dormitory assembly room to officially establish the Glory Group. Yoshinari Yabuki, a tall, good-natured yet strong-willed high school student, was selected as chairperson of the Glory Group's executive committee. Having completed a year in a Tokyo metropolitan high school before entering Soka High School, Yabuki was a year older than his classmates. His family lived in downtown Tokyo, but it was a long commute to the Soka schools campus, so halfway through the first term he became an off-campus boarder.

Yabuki spoke of his aspirations as the committee chairperson: "It is my hope that we, the off-campus boarding students, will work closely together to deepen our friendship and support of each other as we engage in friendly competition toward growth and development. With pride and awareness as a member of Glory Group, I ask your cooperation in building a wonderful tradition for those who will come after us."

YOSHINARI YABUKI'S remarks were filled with strong determination. Some students watched him with surprise; he was a different person from the time he had entered Soka High School.

Yabuki's enrollment in Soka High School was a result of his father Kaoru's fervent prayers. Kaoru Yabuki was a director of the Soka Gakkai, and he had deeply hoped his son would attend the school when it opened. He knew that the Soka schools, into which President Yamamoto had poured his entire life out of the desire to achieve world peace, would be an institution offering truly humanistic education. At the same time, he keenly felt that, as the fruition of the hopes and dreams of the first and second Soka Gakkai presidents, Tsunesaburo Makiguchi and Josei Toda, who had blazed the trail of value-creating education, the schools were a citadel of education realized through the mentor-disciple relationship spanning three generations.

His son Yoshinari, however, was already a freshman at a Tokyo metropolitan high school and seemed to really be enjoying it. Kaoru was certain that Yoshinari would oppose the idea of quitting the school he was attending and taking another entrance exam to study at a place where he would be a year older than his classmates. But Kaoru still hoped that it would happen. He believed that contributing to the school's establishment as a member of its first class would be an unparalleled honor and a precious memory of his son's youth.

From the time Yoshinari began his freshman year at the metropolitan high school, Kaoru prayed earnestly that his son would enter Soka High School the following year. He also took every opportunity he could to speak to his son about how wonderful the new school would be, but he never said anything about sitting for the entrance examination. He knew that if he did, Yoshinari would only rebel against the idea, and he also hoped that his son would arrive at the decision on his own.

However, months passed without Yoshinari ever

mentioning a word about going to Soka High School. In fact, it seemed that he had not even considered it. Kaoru came up with an idea: he asked Yoshinari's private tutor, Yusuke Yamahara, a member of the Soka Gakkai student division, to try to persuade Yoshinari to attend the new school.

Though Yamahara came from a poor family, he had studied hard and gained entrance into the prestigious Tokyo University. Yoshinari respected him.

YAMAHARA ENCOURAGED Yoshinari to sit for the Soka High School entrance exam, but Yoshinari just laughed him off, saying, "What's the point in that?"

Yoshinari's father Kaoru began to do *ushitora* gongyo[8] to pray that Yoshinari would enter Soka High School. Unable to fathom why his father was taking such drastic measures all of a sudden, Yoshinari started to worry that his father's business might be in trouble, and so he asked his mother what was going on.

"Your father is praying earnestly for you to enter Soka High School," she said.

Yoshinari was shocked, and he felt annoyed by his father's selfish concern. In the meantime, Yamahara was coming over to tutor Yoshinari every other day, and while they studied up in Yoshinari's second-floor room, he continued to enthusiastically recommend that his charge attend the new school. But Yoshinari had absolutely no intention of doing so.

On the day before the entrance examination application was due, Yamahara came downstairs after studying with Yoshinari and was greeted by a worried-looking Kaoru, who asked: "Is my son going to sit for the examination?"

Yamahara bowed deeply and said: "I'm sorry. I couldn't persuade him. I really apologize."

Yoshinari came down while this exchange was taking place. He was angry that Yamahara had to apologize to his father. He also felt somewhat responsible and sorry that Yamahara had been put in that position. He suddenly blurted out: "Fine, Dad, if all I have to do is sit for the exam, I will, but don't expect anything else!"

"Really?" Kaoru's face lit up. He had already received the application and made all the necessary arrangements. The next day Yoshinari went to submit the application. He arrived at the Soka schools campus about four o'clock in the afternoon, the deadline for submission. When he delivered the forms, the person behind the window said: "You're just in time. In fact, you're the last applicant." And with that, the window closed.

THE DAY of the entrance examinations arrived. While the students taking the exam busily wrote answers on their test forms, Yoshinari stifled a yawn as he surveyed the others in the room. He intended to hand in a blank test, figuring that just by showing up for the exam, he had fulfilled the promise he made to his father.

As he whiled away the time, Yoshinari happened to glance at the problems. He was taken aback. They were astonishingly difficult—he wasn't even sure if he, a high school freshman, would be able to answer them. Yet the other students were diligently doing so.

These aren't questions third-year junior high students should be able to answer. Who are these guys? he thought. Suddenly a competitive spirit stirred in his heart; he wasn't going to be beaten by anyone younger than him. Before he knew what was happening, he, too, was absorbed in the test.

On the day the test results were announced, Yoshinari still had no intention of entering Soka High School, but he nevertheless wanted to know how he did. He went to see the results and found he had been accepted.

When he got home, his father asked, "How did you do?"

"I passed," Yoshinari replied.

"So you're going to change schools, right?" Kaoru said, as if this was the natural conclusion. Yoshinari was annoyed.

"No, I'm not. I only said I'd take the test."

Kaoru went pale. "That's impossible! The fact that you passed means that someone else failed. That person dreamed of entering the school that President Yama-moto founded, and he studied hard and chanted to get into it. If you don't attend, you're making a mockery of that person's life. You should have a stronger sense of responsibility."

Kaoru was very serious.

Yoshinari thought his father's reasoning was strange, but at the same time he started to feel that he would be doing something wrong if he didn't go. Though it seemed to him that he had been tricked somehow, after much consideration he decided to enter Soka High School.

Once there, however, he had a hard time adapting to the new environment.

TWO DAYS before the entrance ceremony, the new students went to the Soka schools campus to rehearse for the event. Most of them were very proud to be members of the first class and were eager to make the first entrance ceremony a solemn and grand occasion that would go down in history. They rehearsed the school song, as well as standing and sitting in unison, over and over again.

In contrast, the majority of Yoshinari's classmates at his former high school regarded their entrance ceremony with apathy. Accustomed to that attitude, Yoshinari found the atmosphere at Soka High School strange and whispered to the student next to him, "This school is weird, isn't it?"

The student looked at him in astonishment, then glared at him.

I'll never fit in here, Yoshinari thought.

Yoshinari's attitude couldn't have been more different from that of the other students, who seemed to burn with a sense of mission as pioneers of the Soka schools who would shoulder the twenty-first century. This was why he had none of the enthusiasm and passion that they had for the entrance ceremony.

When the first term began, Yoshinari's feelings of isolation only intensified. While others were filled with hope and thoroughly enjoying student life, he was growing more detached. His father Kaoru sensed this and was concerned. He knew it took Yoshinari a long time to commute to and from school, and he was worried that his son was going to announce that he wanted to quit altogether.

Kaoru Yabuki was aware that life decisions such as where one studies must be left to the will of the individual, and that if parents force their children to make such decisions against their wishes, it will only invite significant problems in the future. It was for this reason that, from his perspective, he had done his best to persuade his son to attend Soka High School, while at the same time respecting his son's opinions. And he thought that in the end, Yoshinari had made the decision to attend the school of his own free will. But watching his son grow gloomier day by day, Kaoru was troubled. All he could think to do was chant Nam-myoho-renge-kyo.

ABOUT TWO MONTHS into the first term at Soka High School, Kaoru Yabuki said to his son Yoshinari: "It must be hard to commute to school from home."

"It is," Yoshinari replied. "It takes almost two hours each way."

"Why don't you find a room in a house near the school, then?" Kaoru suggested. "It's a shame to waste all that time you could be studying commuting back and forth to school." Kaoru thought that if Yoshinari lived closer to school, he wouldn't want to stop attending.

So it was that Yoshinari Yabuki began his life as an off-campus boarding student. It was also around that time that he started making new discoveries at school. One was that the teachers were always passionately encouraging students to study and grow for the sake of others, for society and for world peace. No one in his previous school had ever said anything like that. There, the teachers only talked about college entrance examinations and test scores. Their highest goal seemed to be getting as many students as possible into the prestigious University of Tokyo.

Some teachers at his former school even said things like, "If you can't keep up with the class, you belong in night school!" in voices filled with scorn for that alternative. Yoshinari had disagreed with such teachers. In that sense, he was impressed by the sincerity and integrity of the Soka High School faculty.

Another incident that influenced Yoshinari involved a junior high school student from Kagoshima Prefecture who was also living off campus in a house near Yoshinari's. Yoshinari knew about him, but he never made an attempt to reach out to him. Then one day, the teacher responsible for the off-campus boarding students said to

Yoshinari: "Why don't you make an effort to encourage him? He's only a first-year junior high school student, and he's living alone, away from his parents. You're older than him. You shouldn't be so cold. You should be ashamed of yourself for not trying to help your juniors."

Yoshinari had been a top student in junior high, and along the way he had come to care only about improving his grades and forgot the spirit of caring for others. This remark by the teacher made him aware for the first time of his self-centered nature. Even while he was being scolded, he realized that the teacher was speaking the truth. He also felt that any school with teachers who would take the trouble to say something so important must really be a great one.

ANOTHER FACTOR that had a profound impact on Yoshinari was his contact with the school's founder, Shin'ichi Yamamoto, who continued to make significant efforts to support the students. Yoshinari had heard from his father about how incredibly busy President Yamamoto was; yet, whenever he could, that same President Yamamoto traveled to the Soka schools to spend time with the students and speak with them directly. Sometimes he even played tennis or ping-pong with them.

When Shin'ichi missed a volley in a game, he would pretend to be upset and playfully stamp his feet in frustration to make the students laugh. He never put on affectations, but joined the students in their activities and spoke to them as an equal. Furthermore, concerned about the students' health and how they were getting on in their daily lives, he listened to their problems and encouraged them with all his might.

Yoshinari was also impressed by Shin'ichi's thoughtfulness and careful attention to detail. He had heard, for example, that, through the help of faculty members, Shin'ichi made it a point to thank the people in the community who provided lodgings to Soka schools students, even offering them small tokens of appreciation. Yoshinari sensed Shin'ichi's love and hopes for the students, and gradually he felt the desire to respond to such consideration.

Yoshinari came to like his new school and he wanted to do something for it. That's why, when the off-campus boarding student organization Glory Group was formed, he decided to accept the post of chairperson of the group's executive committee.

At the inaugural meeting of Glory Group, Yoshinari announced the new group's motto: "Lifelong Advancement, Lifelong Study, Lifelong Effort and Lifelong Construction." Yoshinari himself had proposed this motto, which he had gleaned from a passage in Shin'ichi's *A Youthful Diary*.[9] For him, it constituted a vow that the off-campus students would live a youth free of regrets so that they could boundlessly make their way into the future, just as Shin'ichi had done when he was a young man living in a boardinghouse.

As chairperson of the executive committee, Yoshinari took the initiative to visit all of the students in the group at their respective lodgings. He put his all into building a strong network of friendship among them through which they could support and encourage each other. Eventually, a firm bond was formed and the boarding students began to feel a sense of pride and awareness as members of the Glory Group.

SHIN'ICHI YAMAMOTO was very concerned about the students whose grades were suffering. Because the teachers were dedicated to fostering the students as leaders of the next generation, the classes moved ahead at a fairly brisk pace and the students had a heavy workload. Shin'ichi suspected that, as a result, some of them must have been struggling to keep up.

After conferring with Principal Takashi Oyamada, Shin'ichi decided to meet with and encourage about thirty high school students who were on the brink of failing their first year. In late December, after the second-term final exams were over, Shin'ichi visited the campus and met with the students together with the schools' general director Kazumasa Morikawa.

Prior to the meeting, the students were told by their teachers that Shin'ichi wanted to speak with those who weren't doing very well. They therefore looked somewhat ashamed when they entered the room, but Shin'ichi greeted them with a broad smile.

"Please don't be nervous," he said. "I didn't come here to scold you. I want to encourage you."

He then proceeded to ask each of the students in detail if anything was troubling them, whether they were in good health, how long their commute to school was and what their situation at home was like. If they were experiencing any problems, Shin'ichi wanted to help them, offer them advice and do whatever he could to support. He also wanted to make the encounter an opportunity to draw forth the students' potential outside of the classroom.

As they spoke with Shin'ichi, many of the students seemed to appreciate and understand his intent. One even pledged on the spot to try harder in his studies. Hearing this, Shin'ichi nodded and smiled warmly as he remarked: "That's right. Do your best. Don't give up. It's important to continually advance, even just a little."

To another, he said: "You mustn't beat yourself up for getting poor marks. Please continue to have a challenging spirit, always striving to do better next time."

"Find one subject you can excel in," he urged others. "Don't be defeated by your own weaknesses."

In this way, Shin'ichi put his entire being into encouraging each student.

The students had worn gloomy expressions when they arrived, but when they left, they looked happy and refreshed.

IT WAS THE TEACHERS who were most amazed by Shin'ichi's actions. Seeing him meet with the struggling students rather than with those who were doing well deeply touched them. They realized that helping even the worst student become the best was the true spirit of value-creating education, and they determined to do their utmost toward that end.

Shin'ichi's encounter with the students turned out to be a great source of inspiration for students and teachers alike. In later years, one of those students would go on to become a university professor.

That same day, Shin'ichi visited the school dormitory and enjoyed a meal with the boarding students. As they ate together, he listened to updates on their activities and encouraged them. After supper, they all went outside and gazed up at the stars in the night sky, while the young people sang their dormitory song.

On the eve of the closing ceremony for the second term, a party was held for the dormitory students before they returned home for the winter break. Though the break was only two weeks long, many of the students were sad to say good-bye to each other and some even shed tears. Having created strong bonds of friendship, they didn't want to part.

One student said to a dorm supervisor: "At first, I was homesick and cried all the time because I wanted to go home, but now I'm having the best time of my life. When I go home, I'm going to tell the other kids there about my wonderful experience at the Soka schools and encourage as many as I can to take the entrance exam. I don't think of myself so much as going home as being sent home on a mission."

An awareness and sense of responsibility as pioneers building the Soka schools was firmly growing in the students' hearts.

The entrance examinations for the second classes of the Soka Junior High School and Soka High School were held in February of the following year, 1969. When the schools asked for volunteers to help with the exams, all of the high school dorm students expressed a strong wish to lend a hand. They played important roles in everything from guiding the prospective new students from the station to the campus, to being liaisons, to help-ing administer first aid. Their friendly, bright attitudes made the students sitting for the exams want to pass even more.

WHILE the examination for the junior high's sec-ond class was taking place, one of the volunteer dormitory students wrote a poem on the dormitory blackboard describing his feelings upon seeing the examinees:

> *With the past year*
> *Engraved in my heart,*
> *I watch the boys*
> *Who will be the second class.*

The next day, when the exam results were announced, one of the examinees' mothers visited the dormitory and saw the poem on the blackboard. She wrote a reply to the poem on behalf of her son, who had been accepted to the school:

> *With the bond*
> *We now forge as brothers,*
> *Please guide me*
> *Inexperienced as I am.*

When the dormitory students learned that it was the mother of one of the new students who had written the poem, they realized just how much the parents of those students counted on them to assist and guide their children. Awakened to their heavy responsibilities as older students, they renewed their commitment and determination.

A total of 205 junior high school and 315 high school students passed the entrance examinations for the second classes of the Soka schools.

In the second year of the Soka schools' inception, Shin'ichi Yamamoto continued to visit the campus regularly. On April 2, he attended the groundbreaking ceremony for Soka University in Hachioji, Tokyo, and from there went directly to the Soka schools. He wanted to share the joy of the university's construction with the young students.

On April 8, he visited the campus again and attended the entrance ceremony for the new school year. After the ceremony, Shin'ichi took commemorative photographs with the entering students. He then changed into a tracksuit and joined the first class students in various games inside the gymnasium to celebrate their advancing to the next grade. When they were finished, Shin'ichi served the students some sweet bean soup.

On this day, Shin'ichi also proposed that they publish a chronicle of the schools' history recording the events of the first year for posterity. Four days later, he invited a total of twenty student and faculty representatives to a Chinese dinner at a Tokyo hotel to discuss the project. One of the reasons he did this was to offer the students, whom he expected to grow into world leaders, opportunities to become familiar with proper dining etiquette.

A second-year junior high school student in the group, Yusuke Kaga, had just lost his mother to cancer five months earlier. When Shin'ichi learned of this from the schools' principal, he thought to himself: *Nothing could be sadder for a thirteen-year-old boy than losing his mother.*

AT THE DINNER, Shin'ichi called Yusuke Kaga aside to speak with him in private: "I heard that your mother passed away," he said.

"That's right," Yusuke replied, tears welling up in his eyes.

Wanting her son to go to the school that President Yamamoto had founded, Yusuke's mother had encouraged him to take the Soka Junior High School entrance examination. And on the day of the entrance ceremony, she sat in the audience smiling as she wiped tears of joy from her eyes. Just the mention of the word *mother* made Yusuke cry.

Shin'ichi said: "Please don't be heartbroken. I'd like you to think of the school as your mother and do your best. There are always difficulties to overcome in life; it's just a matter of when we encounter them. The secret to becoming a great person is triumphing over deep sadness and big problems. This is true of all great men and women.

"I hope you will really do your utmost, without ever giving up. The history of the first year of our schools is also the history of your own life. Let's work on the schools' chronicle together as an expression of gratitude and of your pledge to your mother."

Yusuke nodded, his eyes shining with determination. His was the face of a valiant young champion.

The first editorial meeting for the chronicle was held on May 11, 1969. In addition to Shin'ichi, some twenty faculty members and students participated. In his youth, Shin'ichi had worked for Josei Toda's publishing company as the managing editor of a boy's magazine, and he wanted to share his thoughts on editing and its rewards.

It was a lively discussion. While responding to the students' questions, Shin'ichi also discussed literature and the joys of reading, turning the meeting into a memorable special lecture by the schools' founder. In addition, Shin'ichi agreed to submit an article for the chronicle. On June 15, he attended another editorial meeting, at which the title of the schools' history was decided: *The Soka Schools: A Year of Construction*.

Shin'ichi paid a surprise visit to the campus again six days later, on June 21. Stopping in to see the students proofreading the draft, he looked over the galley proofs with them and spoke to them of the importance of developing their proofreading skills.

ONE MORNING during this period of regular visits to the Soka schools, Shin'ichi's wife, Mineko, said to him: "Dear, you're going to the Soka schools today, aren't you?"

Shin'ichi hadn't mentioned anything about his plans for the day to Mineko yet.

"How did you know?" he asked.

"I can tell," she said. "On the days you're going to visit the campus, there's always more of a bounce in your step. You seem happier than usual."

That was true, Shin'ichi thought. Supporting the growth of the Soka schools' students was his greatest purpose in life, and he gave his all to it, caring for them and nurturing them with his whole heart. When he knew he was going to be seeing them he was filled with joy and excitement.

On July 17, 1969, when the first-term exams were over, the second Glory Festival was held. This event initially took place specifically for dormitory students the year before, but from this year it became a school festival for all students.

The previous day had seen the launching of the US spacecraft *Apollo 11* on its mission of the first lunar landing. With this in mind, Shin'ichi arrived at the school a little before five o'clock in the evening for the festival, his thoughts set on the future awaiting the students.

A teacher greeted Shin'ichi on his arrival, saying, "It's finished at last!" and handed him several copies of the new school history, *The Soka Schools: A Year of Construction.* As he turned the pages of the volume, Shin'ichi smiled and said with great feeling, "It's a fine book."

He then headed for the athletic field where the festival was being held under the theme, "Glorious Youth."

Twelve years earlier, Shin'ichi had been unjustly arrested and imprisoned by the authorities. This was due to the fact that the sudden emergence of the Soka Gakkai as a powerful popular force was seen as a threat to the establishment. While in prison, Shin'ichi battled the devilish nature of authority, vowing to continue this struggle as long as he lived for the sake of the people's victory. He was released on July 17, this very day they were holding the Soka schools' festival. Shin'ichi wanted the students gathered for the festival to become leaders who would carry on his vision. In fact, he was certain they would.

A special stage had been built in the center of the athletic field, on which hung a backdrop with the image of an eagle powerfully spreading its wings.

THE GLORY FESTIVAL began after Shin'ichi took his seat with the other spectators on the athletic field. The first part of the festival involved traditional song and dance. Since Soka schools' students hailed from all over Japan, they performed a wide variety of indigenous songs and dances from every region of the country, reaching from Hokkaido in the north to Kagoshima in the south. The second part of the festival included contemporary folk songs, pantomimes and skits. For the finale, all of the participants performed the "Glory Festival

Dance," which was specially choreographed for the festival, and sang the dormitory song together.

Every detail of the program had been well thought-out and prepared. The students' creativity and ingenuity was evident from beginning to end. Their performances overflowed with vigor and the passion of youth. Shin'-ichi was delighted to see that in the fifteen months since the schools' establishment, the students were showing such remarkable growth.

When they had finished singing the dormitory song, the students gathered in front of Shin'ichi. He said to them: "Thank you for your performances! My true purpose in life, the undertaking that constitutes my life's work, is raising leaders who will be celebrated in the next century. The only way to achieve this goal is through education. Therefore, from now on, my greatest effort will be devoted to this endeavor.

"As the founder of these schools, I continue to pray with all my heart that you will grow solidly, like strong and mighty trees. Please do your best!"

"We will!" the students replied energetically.

Dusk began to descend over Musashino. The more than one thousand students present listened intently to Shin'ichi's words, their eyes sparkling and their expressions serious.

"You are the leaders of the twenty-first century who will act out your lives on the stage of the twenty-first century. There are about thirty years remaining until that century dawns. You will all be in your forties then. I am now forty-one. The next ten to fifteen years will be the prime of my life. You will start the twenty-first century at about the same age I am now. You will begin that new century at the peak of your lives."

Shin'ichi looked into the distance, as if gazing into the future.

SHIN'ICHI YAMAMOTO continued: "I believe that by the beginning of the twenty-first century, many of you—the members of the Soka schools' first two classes—will be leaders in your respective fields, whether it be as company presidents or directors, or as journalists, scientists, artists or doctors. Others will likely be active as leaders among ordinary people, living modest yet brilliant lives.

"I'd like to propose that the more than one thousand pioneering Soka schools' students and faculty members gathered here today all come together for a reunion on July 17, 2001. How about it?"

Everyone cheered their approval, their voices ringing out as pledges, into the evening sky.

Shin'ichi further remarked that while the students were certain to encounter all manner of trials and challenges in their lives, he hoped they would face and overcome each one as part of their training as leaders. He then urged: "Let us make the year 2001 one of our targets. Let no one be defeated on the way to that goal. I hope we can all gather at that time in good health and as people making significant contributions to the world. The lion's cubs are all lions, too. It thus follows that those who study at the Soka schools all have wonderful missions. The true glory of life is found in carrying out our life's purpose in our own capacity.

"Fundamentally, material wealth and social status are irrelevant. What matters is how you shine as a human being. I will be looking forward to our encounter in 2001, continuing my endeavors to open the way for you as I warmly watch over your efforts from the sidelines. That is my greatest joy and the purpose of my life. With that in mind, please live your lives boldly and with great vigor."

When the festival had ended, Shin'ichi waved to the students until every last one of them had left the field. Though they had agreed to a reunion in 2001, they didn't fully comprehend the significance of their promise. They did, however, keenly feel the spirit of their schools' founder, who was dedicating his life to raising capable people to work for world peace in the twenty-first century, and they wanted to respond to his expectations.

The Glory Festival became the occasion when the Soka schools' students made their lifetime pledges and it marked the start of their journey into the twenty-first century.

SHIN'ICHI CONTINUED to devote all his energy to fostering the students. He made it possible for a group of students and teachers to visit the United States during summer vacation of that year, 1969, in an effort to cultivate the students' awareness of the world. He also carried on with his regular visits to the schools, and sometimes would introduce the students to leading world figures, such as Count Richard Coudenhove-Kalergi, the Austrian thinker and early proponent of European unification.

On one occasion, Shin'ichi proposed that the students organize a haiku gathering in which everyone would compose a poem, and he participated in the event. In addition, he would accompany the students on camping trips to the ocean or the woods, and would swim and fish with them. On those trips, he would prepare their baths for them, check in on them while they slept and cover them with blankets in the middle of the night so they wouldn't catch cold.

Shin'ichi had firmly determined that should any of the students suffer setbacks in life, he would be there to encourage and watch over them to the very end of his days.

In the more than thirty-year history of the Soka schools, there were in fact some students who got into trouble and were expelled. Whenever such a thing happened, Shin'ichi prayed earnestly for those students. One autumn, when Shin'ichi was visiting the campus, he learned that two third-year junior school high students living in the dormitory had been dismissed for improper behavior and were being sent back to their homes in Osaka. He immediately borrowed a room on the second floor of the residence hall to talk with them.

They came to the tiny dorm room and sat stiffly in front of Shin'ichi, so close that their knees almost touched his. Shin'ichi would have liked to override their expulsion, but he knew he couldn't bend the rules, and it wouldn't be right to contradict the principal's authority. He looked at the boys, who would not meet his gaze.

When they had started at the school, surely their eyes shone brightly and their hearts were filled with hope.

Now they were being forced to leave without completing their studies. The thought pained Shin'ichi and he felt terribly sorry for them. It also broke his heart to think how their parents must feel.

"I don't want these two boys to be unhappy. I will watch over them for the rest of my life," Shin'ichi decided.

SHIN'ICHI SPOKE with all his heart to the two boys seated before him: "No matter what happens, remember that I am always on your side. When I am in Osaka, please come together to see me. Promise me you'll come without fail. All right?"

Shin'ichi prayed sincerely for their growth as he watched them leave the room.

About two years later, when Shin'ichi was visiting Osaka, the youths came to see him at the Kansai Culture Center. Actually, they had been urged to do so by their families, who wanted them to keep their promise to Shin'ichi. Both of them wore leather jackets, and one had an Elvis Presley-style haircut. The culture center reception staff were put off by their tough appearance, and they had to do considerable explaining before they were allowed in to meet Shin'ichi. But Shin'ichi was overjoyed that they had kept their word to come and see him.

"Thank you for coming! I'm so glad you did!" he said.

They began to talk in the culture center lobby. The young men explained that they were now attending local Osaka high schools. Shin'ichi was very concerned about their plans after graduation. "Are you going to college?" he asked.

"I'm no good at English, so I won't be accepted," one answered. "I'll get a job."

Jokingly, Shin'ichi responded: "But you're so fluent in the Osaka dialect that it seems to me English should be no problem for you!"

This broke the ice.

"Sensei, it's not the same thing," the youth replied with a smile.

"Oh. I guess not," Shin'ichi conceded.

Both young men smiled broadly.

"Everyone doesn't have to go to college I suppose," Shin'ichi remarked. "The important thing is to win in whatever path you choose for yourself."

And with that Shin'ichi gave them a small gift of money from his personal funds.

"It was so nice to see you," he said. "Let's meet again. Make sure to come back the next time I'm in town. And please take good care of your parents."

"We will!" they said, happily nodding.

Shin'ichi's love for them knew no bounds.

AS THEY PROMISED, the two boys who had been expelled from Soka Junior High School continued to visit Shin'ichi Yamamoto whenever he came to Osaka, and Shin'ichi welcomed them warmly each time. Over the years, Shin'ichi noticed them grow brighter and more positive. After graduating from high school, both took jobs as subway drivers. They earned respect and trust at their workplace and also became active leaders of the local young men's division.

To Shin'ichi, anyone who had once attended the Soka schools was still his precious charge. He cared for them as if they were his own children. And he continued to encourage all of the students long after their time at the schools was over.

One such student was Yoshinari Yabuki, the young man who had taken responsibility as leader of the off-campus boarding students. Yabuki went on to play an active role in various Soka schools activities, and after graduating entered the economics department of the newly founded Soka University in 1971. As a member of the university's first class, he gave his all to helping lay the school's foundation.

After graduating from Soka University in 1975, he attended Gustavus Adolphus College in Minnesota, in the United States, as a foreign student. Though apprehensive at first, he quickly found that he enjoyed studying abroad. Initially, he received many letters from his friends in Japan, but as the year wore on and winter neared, their correspondence dwindled and finally stopped altogether.

Winter in Minnesota was very cold, with the temperature sometimes dropping as low as minus twenty-two degrees Fahrenheit. Yabuki was struggling with learning English and his classes were difficult. He started to feel overwhelmed, as if being oppressed by the approaching winter. Without anyone close by from whom he could seek advice, he was terribly lonely. When he thought of the fact that many of his friends back in Japan were making great strides in their respective fields, he began to feel as if he were being left behind.

THE COLD grew fiercer by the day. One day, Yabuki checked his campus mailbox as usual. It had been a while since any letters had come from Japan, but when his classes ended he would habitually check the box, always with a slight sense of anticipation. Most days it was empty, and he was forced to swallow his disappointment.

But today there was a letter. He took it out and looked at the return address. "Shin'ichi Yamamoto" was typed in Roman letters. "This can't be from President Yamamoto!" Yabuki thought incredulously. His heart pounded as he opened it. There in front of him was the familiar handwriting of President Yamamoto in blue ink.

His eyes pored over the page:

Dear Mr. Yabuki,
As my disciple, I hope you will advance resolutely, keeping your focus thirty years hence. Please don't

forget that many more of my disciples will follow after you. You have a great responsibility and mission. Though you may have to make personal sacrifices along the way, it is important to boldly open the path for those who will come after you.

I pray for your good health and your development.

Shin'ichi

Tears clouded Yabuki's vision as he read. He stood there for some time, the letter in his hands. *I thought I was forgotten about all the way over here in distant America, but I was just being swept up in my emotions. Nothing has changed with Yamamoto Sensei. He has kept me in his heart.*

Wiping his tears, Yabuki reread the letter. He read it over and over, as if to etch it into his life.

That's right, he thought. *Just as Sensei says, I am here for*

*the sake of the thousands and tens of thousands of Soka schools
and Soka University students who will come after me. I cannot
allow myself to be defeated!*

As Yabuki said these words to himself, he became filled
with courage and energy.

SHIN'ICHI CONTINUED to encourage Yoshinari Yabuki whenever the young man returned
home to Japan or when Shin'ichi traveled to the United
States. He told Yabuki: "Please study hard and earn a PhD
in preparation for the day when I found a Soka University in the United States."

Shin'ichi said this at a time when Soka University in
Japan was still just getting off the ground. No one be-
lieved that such a school would actually be built in
America. Yabuki, however, accepted this dream as an
eventual reality and energetically pursued his studies to-
ward its actualization. After nine years of study in the
United States, he obtained a PhD from Washington State
University.

Shin'ichi believed that the starting point and essence
of Soka (value-creating) education was the spirit to value
each student's individuality so that they could become
happy and enjoy a glorious future. Education does not
exist for the sake of the nation, for business or for religion. The aim of Soka education is the happiness of oneself and others, as well as society as a whole and peace for
all humanity.

Based on that spirit, the system of Soka education was
gradually put into place, beginning with the establishment of the Soka Junior High School and Soka High

School in Tokyo in 1968. Next came Soka University in Hachioji, Tokyo, in 1971. In 1973, the Soka Girls Junior High School and Soka Girls High School opened in Katano, Osaka. In 1976, the Sapporo Soka Kindergarten opened in Sapporo, Hokkaido. In 1978, Tokyo Soka Elementary School opened in Kodaira City, Tokyo. In 1982, the Soka Junior High School and Soka High School went coeducational. The Soka Girls Junior High School and Soka Girls High School in Osaka followed suit, changing their name to Kansai Soka Junior High School and Kansai Soka High School. At the same time, the Kansai Soka Elementary School opened in Hirakata City, Osaka. In 1985, Soka Women's College opened on the grounds of Soka University.

Soka schools were eventually established around the world, with kindergartens opening in Hong Kong in 1992, Singapore in 1993, Malaysia in 1995 and Brazil in 2001.

IN THE UNITED STATES, the Los Angeles campus of Soka University opened in February 1987. In September 1994, it started as a graduate school under the name of Soka University of America (SUA). Then, on May 3, 2001, SUA, Aliso Viejo, opened in Southern California's Orange County, adopting the mottoes: 1) Be philosophers of a renaissance of life; 2) Be world citizens in solidarity for peace and 3) Be pioneers of a global civilization. Hence, SUA, Aliso Viejo, embarked on its course as a full-fledged liberal arts college. Appointed as the president of the new university was none other than Yoshinari Yabuki.

Other graduates of the Soka Junior High School and Soka High School also vigorously pursued their chosen fields in life, aiming for their goal of the 2001 reunion that Shin'ichi Yamamoto had proposed at the second Glory Festival in 1969. On September 16, 2001, the Soka schools Twenty-first Century Gathering was held. Some thirty-two hundred representative alumni, not only from the schools' first two classes but up to the eighteenth class, assembled at their alma mater from across Japan, as well as from sixteen countries and territories around the world.

Thirty-three years had passed since their schools were founded. Having begun their life's journeys from the Soka schools, many of the graduates were making significant contributions to society. Now they had returned to the home of Soka education. Among the graduates there were 140 medical doctors, 111 PhDs, 60 attorneys and others in the legal profession, 60 certified public accountants and 462 elementary and secondary school teachers. There were also company presidents, journalists and political leaders.

Shin'ichi stood on the stage in the gymnasium where the reunion was taking place and beheld the gathering of Soka schools alumni. They had all developed into great phoenixes and fulfilled their vow to him. He wanted to engrave the faces of each of them, his successors, in his mind.

It was a reunion of global citizens, with guests from the Sakha Republic of the Russian Federation; a delegation from a women's college in India that had adopted the ideals of Soka education and been named after Shin'ichi;

and other non-Japanese guests who had come to offer their congratulations.

Promising to hold another reunion in 2005 to commemorate the seventy-fifth anniversary of the birth of Soka education in 1930, Shin'ichi presented the alumni with a poem:

> *Rejoicing at*
> *Your tremendous growth,*
> *I applaud you*
> *Wholeheartedly—*
> *You have triumphed.*

NOTES

1. Musashino: Area of western Tokyo famous for its natural beauty.

2. Jishu Gakkan: An elementary tutorial school founded by Josei Toda in 1923 as a place to prove through experimentation Tsunesaburo Makiguchi's theory of value-creating education.

3. The Soka Junior High School and Soka High School were first established for boys in 1968. The following year, plans were announced for the establishment of girls' schools, which opened in Osaka in 1973. In 1982, both the Tokyo and Kansai institutions became coeducational.

4. Makiguchi advocated that happiness is founded on the pursuit of value, and he set forth "beauty, benefit and good" as the values human beings should strive to create in the course of their lives.

5. In this system, students would engage in formal study for half of the day and have access to practical vocational training in the other half. Through this proposal, Makiguchi emphasized

the importance of building a society centered on lifetime learning.

6. Inazo Nitobe (1862–1933).

7. Old-system high schools: Three-year educational institutions that were in existence until the educational reforms of 1947. Students lived in dormitories as they prepared to enter imperial universities.

8. *Ushitora* gongyo: An early morning recitation of the sutra conducted between the hour of the ox (*ushi*) and the tiger (*tora*) [between around two o'clock and four o'clock in the morning] to pray for the realization for world peace.

9. Daisaku Ikeda, *A Youthful Diary: One Man's Journey from the Beginning of Faith to Worldwide Leadership for Peace* (Santa Monica, California: World Tribune Press, 2000), p 191.

Index

More on Nichiren Buddhism
and Its Application to Daily Life

The following eleven titles can be purchased from your local or On-line bookseller, or go to the Middleway Press Web site (www.middlewaypress.com).

Buddhism Day by Day: Wisdom for Modern Life
by Daisaku Ikeda
This treasury of practical information and encouragement will appeal to those seeking a deeper understanding of how to apply the tenets of Nichiren Buddhism in their day-to-day lives.
(Paperback: ISBN-13: 978-0-9723267-5-9; $15.95)

Buddhism for You: Courage
In this oasis of insight and advise on the power of Nichiren Buddhism—which holds that everyone has a Buddha nature of limitless power, wisdom and compassion—readers will learn how to live a life filled with courage, determination, love and prayer to achieve their goals and desires. This book focuses on the power of *courage* and its role in achieving happiness.
(Hardcover: ISBN-13: 978-0-9723267-6-6; $7.95)

Buddhism for You: Determination

In this oasis of insight and advise on the power of Nichiren Buddhism—which holds that everyone has a Buddha nature of limitless power, wisdom and compassion—readers will learn how to live a life filled with courage, determination, love and prayer to achieve their goals and desires. This book focuses on the power of *determination* and its role in achieving happiness.

(Hardcover: ISBN-13: 978-0-9723267-8-0; $7.95)

Buddhism for You: Love

In this oasis of insight and advise on the power of Nichiren Buddhism—which holds that everyone has a Buddha nature of limitless power, wisdom and compassion—readers will learn how to live a life filled with courage, determination, love and prayer to achieve their goals and desires. This book focuses on the power of *love* and its role in achieving happiness.

(Hardcover: ISBN-13: 978-0-9723267-7-3; $7.95)

Buddhism for You: Prayer

In this oasis of insight and advise on the power of Nichiren Buddhism—which holds that everyone has a Buddha nature of limitless power, wisdom and compassion—readers will learn how to live a life filled with courage, determination, love and prayer to achieve their goals and desires. This book focuses on the power of *prayer* and its role in achieving happiness.

(Hardcover: ISBN-13: 978-0-9723267-9-7; $7.95)

The Buddha in Your Mirror: Practical Buddhism and the Search for Self, by Woody Hochswender, Greg Martin and Ted Morino

A bestselling Buddhist primer that reveals the most modern, effective and practical way to achieve what is called enlightenment or Buddhahood. Based on the centuries-old teaching of the Japanese Buddhist master Nichiren, this method has been called the "direct path" to enlightenment. (Paperback: ISBN-13: 0-978-9674697-8-2; $14.00, Hardcover: ISBN-13: 0-978-9674697-1-3; $23.95)

Choose Hope: Your Role in Waging Peace in the Nuclear Age, by David Krieger and Daisaku Ikeda

"In this nuclear age, when the future of humankind is imperiled by irrational strategies, it is imperative to restore sanity to our policies and hope to our destiny. Only a rational analysis of our problems can lead to their solution. This book is an example par excellence of a rational approach."
—Joseph Rotblat, Nobel Peace Prize laureate
(Hardcover: ISBN-13: 978-0-9674697-6-8; $23.95)

Planetary Citizenship: *Your* **Values, Beliefs and Actions** *Can* **Shape a Sustainable World**
by Hazel Henderson and Daisaku Ikeda

"*Planetary Citizenship* is a delightful introduction to some of the most important ideas and facts concerning stewardship of the planet. I cannot think of any book that deals with more important issues."
—Mihaly Csikszentmihalyi, author of *Flow: The Psychology of Optimal Experience,* California
(Hardcover: ISBN-13: 978-0-9723267-2-8; $23.95)

Romancing the Buddha: Embracing Buddhism in My Everyday Life by Michael Lisagor

"*Romancing the Buddha: Embracing Buddhism in My Everyday Life* is…a resource which provides excellent insights into applying Nichiren Buddhism to the difficulties of daily life, including depression, spousal illness, the challenge of raising two daughters and the quest for happiness. An absorbing and inspirational selection of vignettes touched with wisdom, *Romancing the Buddha* is an impressive and welcome contribution to Buddhist Studies reading lists."
—Midwest Book Review
(Paperback: ISBN-13: 978-0-9723267-4-2; $18.95)

Unlocking the Mysteries of Birth & Death…and Everything in Between, A Buddhist View of Life (second edition) by Daisaku Ikeda

"In this slender volume, Ikeda presents a wealth of profound information in a clear and straightforward style that can be easily absorbed by the interested lay reader. His life's work, and the underlying purpose of his book, is simply to help human beings derive maximum meaning from their lives through the study of Buddhism."
—ForeWord Magazine
(Paperback: ISBN-13: 978-0-9723267-0-4; $15.00)

The Way of Youth: Buddhist Common Sense for Handling Life's Questions, by Daisaku Ikeda

"[This book] shows the reader how to flourish as a young person in the world today; how to build confidence and character in modern society; learn to live with respect for oneself and others; how to contribute to a positive, free and peaceful society; and find true personal happiness."
—Midwest Book Review
(Paperback: ISBN-13: 978-0-9674697-0-6; $14.95)

The following titles can be purchased at SGI-USA
bookstores nationwide or through the mail order center:
call 800-626-1313 or e-mail mailorder@sgi-usa.org.

Commentaries on Buddhahood: Lessons on the Writings of Nichiren Daishonin by the Soka Gakkai Study Department
These booklets contain lectures, originally given by SGI Study Department Leader Katsuji Saito for the SGI North America Leaders Study Conference held from July 15–17, 2005, on the following writings of Nichiren Daishonin. (World Tribune Press; $2.00 each booklet)

"On Attaining Buddhahood in This Lifetime," mail order #4901
"The Heritage of the Ultimate Law of Life," mail order #4902
"Letter from Sado," mail order #4903
"On the True Aspect of All Phenomena," mail order #4904

Faith into Action: Thoughts on Selected Topics, by Daisaku Ikeda
A collection of inspirational excerpts arranged by subject. Perfect for finding just the right quote to encourage yourself or a friend or when preparing for a meeting. (World Tribune Press, mail order #4135; $12.95)

The Human Revolution, boxed set by Daisaku Ikeda
"A great human revolution in just a single individual will help achieve a change in the destiny of a nation, and further, can even enable a change in the destiny of all humankind." With this as his main theme, the author wrote his twelve-volume account of Josei Toda's life and the phenomenal

growth of the Soka Gakkai in postwar Japan. Published in a slightly abridged two-book set, this work paints a fascinating and empowering story of the far-reaching effects of one person's inner determination. Josei Toda's awakening and transformation, his efforts to teach others the unlimited power of faith, his dedication in leading thousands out of misery and poverty, the efforts of his devoted disciple Shin'-ichi Yamamoto—within these stories we find the keys for building lives of genuine happiness.

(World Tribune Press, mail order #4182; $45.00)

The Journey Begins: First Steps in Buddhist Practice

A pamphlet on the basics of Nichiren Daishonin's Buddhism. Each step is discussed in very basic terms, but each plays an important role in your practice. For the new member, the points will help you build a foundation in your practice. Return to them again and again throughout your practice to help keep yourself on track and get the maximum benefit from your Buddhist practice.

(World Tribune Press, $1.00 per pamphlet)

[Chinese] mail order #4186

[English] mail order #4138

[French] mail order #4188

[Spanish] mail order #4139

My Dear Friends in America, by Daisaku Ikeda

This volume brings together for the first time all of the SGI president's speeches to US members in the 1990s.

(World Tribune Press, mail order #4104; $19.95)

The New Human Revolution, by Daisaku Ikeda

An ongoing novelized history of the Soka Gakkai, which contains not only episodes from the past but guidance in faith that we can apply as we grow our movement here in the United States.

(World Tribune Press; $12.00 each volume)
Volume 1, mail order #4601
Volume 2, mail order #4602
Volume 3, mail order #4603
Volume 4, mail order #4604
Volume 5, mail order #4605
Volume 6, mail order #4606
Volume 7, mail order #4607
Volume 8, mail order #4608
Volume 9, mail order #4609
Volume 10, mail order #4610
Volume 11, mail order #4611
Volume 12, mail order #4612

The Winning Life:
An Introduction to Buddhist Practice

Using plain language, this booklet gives a quick-yet-detailed introduction to a winning way of life based on Nichiren Daishonin's teachings. A perfect tool for introducing other to the benefits of practice.

(World Tribune Press, $1.00 per booklet)
[Armenian] mail order #4189
[Chinese] mail order #4107
[English] mail order #4105
[French] mail order #4187
[Japanese] mail order #4815
[Korean] mail order #4113
[Spanish] mail order #4106

The Wisdom of the Lotus Sutra, vols. 1–6, by Daisaku
Ikeda, Katsuji Saito, Takanori Endo and Haruo Suda
A captivating dialogue on the twenty-eight-chapter Lotus
Sutra that brings this ancient writing's important messages
into practical application for daily life and for realizing a
peaceful world.
(World Tribune Press, $10.95 per volume)
Volume 1, mail order #4281
Volume 2, mail order #4282
Volume 3, mail order #4283
Volume 4, mail order #4284
Volume 5, mail order #4285
Volume 6, mail order #4286

The World of Nichiren Daishonin's Writings
by Daisaku Ikeda, Katsuji Saito and Masaaki Morinaka
These books bring to life the teachings and major life
events of Nichiren Daishonin's through an ongoing discus-
sion between SGI President Ikeda, Soka Gakkai Study
Department Leader Katsuji Saito and Study Department
Vice Leader Masaaki Morinaka. Revitalize our pursuit of
creating happiness and peace with this four-volume series.
(SGI Malaysia, $7.95 per volume)
Volume 1, mail order #1891
Volume 2, mail order #1892
Volume 3, mail order #1893
Volume 4, mail order #1894

**A Youthful Diary: One Man's Journey From the
Beginning of Faith to Worldwide Leadership for
Peace,** by Daisaku Ikeda
Youthful inspiration for people of all ages. Through the tale

of the ever-deepening relationship between the young Daisaku Ikeda and his mentor-in-life, Josei Toda, *A Youthful Diary* is a compelling account of both triumphs and setbacks on the road to establishing the foundation of today's Soka Gakkai.

(World Tribune Press, Hardcover: mail order #4101; $23.95, Paperback: mail order #4120; $15.00)